THE WISDOM OF CURIOSITY

52 weeks of why and wonder

Atria SENIOR LIVING

FOR OUR DEAR RESIDENTS,
WHO IN CONTINUING TO LEARN AND GROW,
INSPIRE US TO DO THE SAME.

– YOUR ATRIA FAMILY

ACKNOWLEDGMENTS

Pirates Ahoy – Front cover / Les Graves / Hulton Archive / Getty Images

Group of people watching magician, state fair, Donaldsonville, Louisiana – Inside front cover
Lee, Russell. LC-USF33-011788-M5. Photograph. Lib. of Cong., Washington D.C.

Kopp – Page 78 Bain News Service. LC-DIG-ggbain-35110. Photograph. Lib. of Cong., Washington D.C.

Boy Holds School Door Open for Girl, 1965 – Page 120 Lambert / Archive Photos / Getty Images

Young Shoppers – Page 130 Fox Photos / Hulton Archive / Getty Images

Drain Check – Inside back cover Lambert / Archive Photos / Getty Images

ENGAGE LIFE®

People belong together. Along with nutrition, exercise and goal setting, relationships are essential to our overall well-being.

At Atria, we call our events program Engage Life because that's exactly what we've designed it to help our residents do every day, in the company of friends.

For the people who call us home, *The Wisdom of Curiosity* is much more than a planner. It's the foundation of an entire year's worth of meaningful opportunities to learn, grow and challenge themselves in our communities.

We invite you to learn more about us and follow our curious adventures throughout the year.

AtriaSeniorLiving.com

My friends Susan, Jerry and Alan, and me (on the right), age 11.

"What's tennis?"
That simple, two-word reply to my friend Susan's invitation to play tennis in the fifth grade was the moment my career began and my life changed. I could have said "no thanks" since I didn't know what she was talking about. Instead, *I asked a question* – one that ended up determining the path I chose in life. I was curious then, and my curiosity has helped me continue to grow and succeed ever since.

We are meant to keep exploring, learning and trying new things throughout our lives. Each new day is an opportunity to be challenged, solve problems and fully engage in what we choose to do. This is especially important as we grow older and work to prevent decline and keep moving forward.

My relationship with Atria Senior Living began when I visited one of their communities during my search for a better way for my own family to manage. As soon as I walked in the door, it was clear to me that something different and exciting was going on. This was a vibrant community where older people were having fun, participating and doing all kinds of interesting things together. It was a place that shared my values and my vision for the kind of life I wanted for my family member – and for all of us as we age.

From that point on, I have been thrilled to partner with Atria and serve as their Well-Being Coach. *The Wisdom of Curiosity* is a perfect example of how Atria not only reveres and celebrates their residents' extraordinary lives – they are committed to helping them continue to grow, express themselves and keep learning every day.

It has been my privilege to visit with Atria residents throughout the country and encourage them to be champions of their own well-being – to stay active, connected and engaged, and to keep making a positive difference in our world.

Atria residents and employees inspire me, too. They know that being older and wiser doesn't mean you stop being curious. In fact, it's the time to be more curious than ever.

Billie Jean King
Winner of 39 Grand Slam Tennis Titles
Champion for Social Change and Equality
Atria's Well-Being Coach

“THE MIND IS NOT A VESSEL TO BE FILLED, BUT A FIRE TO BE KINDLED.”

PLUTARCH

The thing about wisdom is,
the wiser you are, the more
you realize just how much
more there is to know – and
that there's still more you
don't even know that you
don't know. You appreciate
the beauty in both the
mystery and the discovery.
That's curiosity.

Curiosity leads to greater
well-being because it
helps give us purpose.
The promise of learning
something we didn't know,
meeting interesting people
or discovering a new passion
keeps us moving forward.

The Wisdom of Curiosity is a planner designed to help you continue to exercise your mighty curiosity muscle, grow even wiser and experience greater well-being in the year ahead. There's calendar space, too, so you can keep track of the appointments that help you stay healthy, and the events and holidays you're looking forward to celebrating.

Wonder of the Week

Each calendar page contains a thought-provoking exercise in curiosity to explore and contemplate as you go about the next seven days.

Wisdom of the Week

You'll also find suggestions on how to further consider the exercise and reflect on the insights you've gained after you've had a week to wonder and ponder.

Well-Being Check-In

Studies have shown that 70 percent of our overall well-being as we age is determined by four key lifestyle choices: **exercise, connection, nutrition and goals**. Curiosity helps us consistently make better choices because it keeps us looking forward and challenging ourselves.

On each weekly calendar page you'll find a space dedicated to helping you track your well-being using the "smiley scale."

At the end of the week, take a few moments to give yourself an *honest* assessment of your lifestyle choices by drawing an expression that represents how you're feeling about them in the little blank face next to each statement.

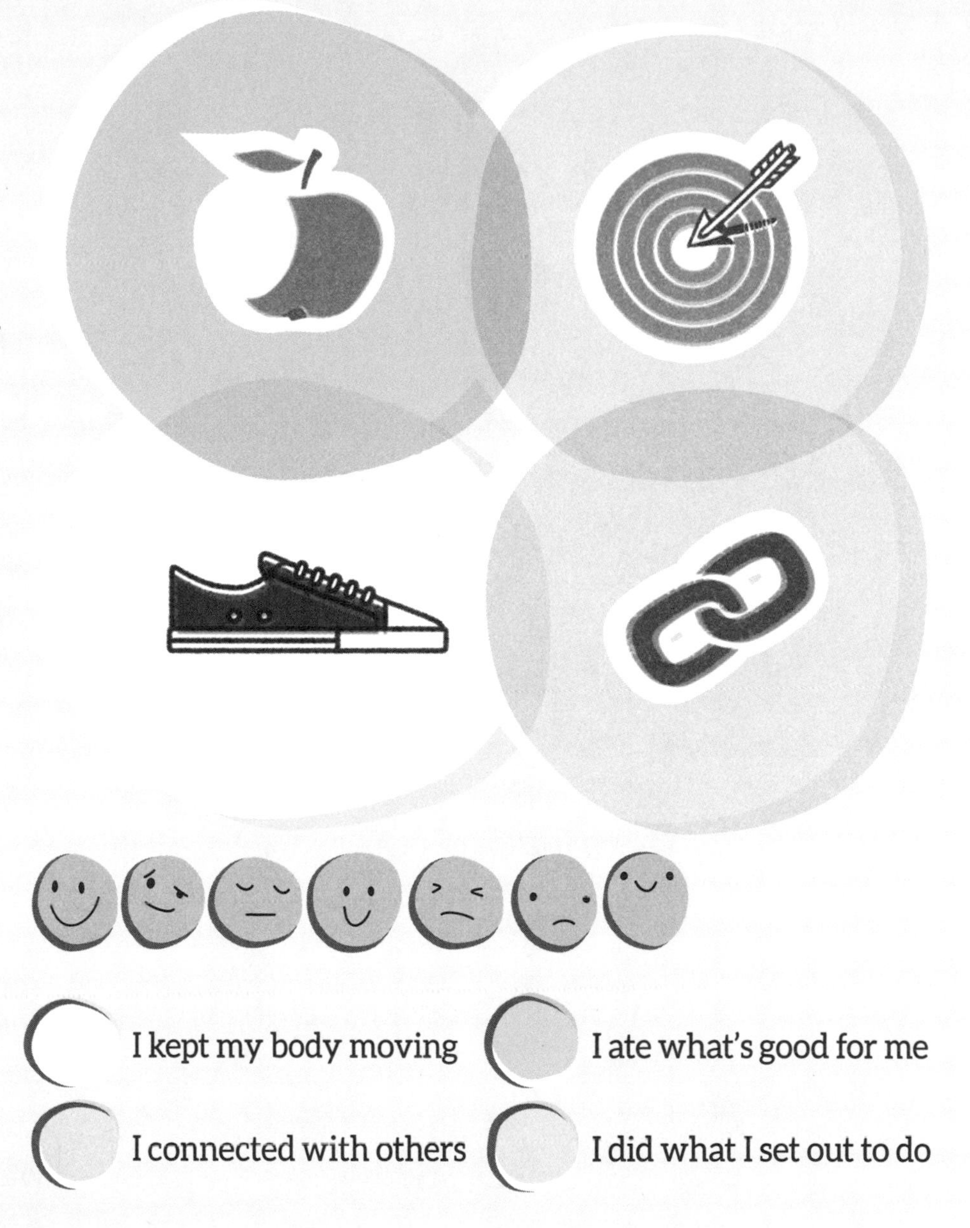

How well is your being?

At the end of every month, you'll have the opportunity to reflect on your achievements and goals, work on solutions to any bumps in the road and make your plan for the weeks to come.

Postcards

Curiosity is best when it's shared. We have included a unique assortment of postcards in your planner's back pocket to help you share your experiences and spread the wisdom of curiosity with your favorite people.

What if you could talk to your future self?

You receive a mysterious letter, postmarked December 31, **2017**.
Turns out, it's from your **future self**, and it's filled with news of the past year's events in your world, all the ways you grew and all the things you learned.

Write what you want that letter to say below.

Dear Me,

Hello, I hope you are doing well. I can't wait to share with you what an amazing year I have had.

I'm so grateful for the many good things, like ____________________,
____________________ and ____________________.

My number one priority over the past year was ____________________
____________________,
and I worked really hard to achieve it.

I'm so proud of myself for finally trying ____________________.

And I'm glad I decided to get back in touch with ____________________.

I have been more disciplined about ____________________,
and most days I feel ____________________.

In a word, 2017 was ____________________.

With gratitude for a great year,
Future Self

"IF YOU DON'T KNOW WHERE YOU ARE GOING, YOU'LL END UP SOMEPLACE ELSE."

YOGI BERRA

Wisdom of the Week

What about the new year most excites you? Why?

1 SUNDAY New Year's Day

2 MONDAY

3 TUESDAY

4 WEDNESDAY

5 THURSDAY

6 FRIDAY

7 SATURDAY

Well-Being Check-In

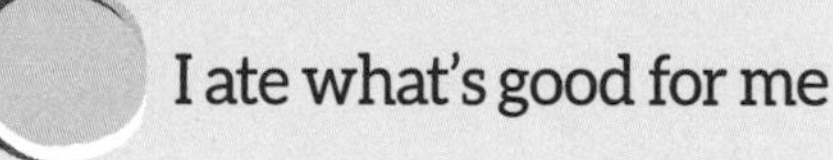

I kept my body moving

I ate what's good for me

I connected with others

I did what I set out to do

S	M	T	W	T	F	S
1	2	3	4	5	6	7
8	9	10	11	12	13	14
15	16	17	18	19	20	21
22	23	24	25	26	27	28
29	30	31	1	2	3	4

Take the silly test.

We all need to give ourselves permission to be silly once in a while. This week, surrender to your inner goofball. Make a different funny face in the mirror each morning, then use it as you greet people throughout the day.

**“’Twas brillig, and the slithy toves
Did gyre and gimble in the wabe;
All mimsy were the borogoves,
And the mome raths outgrabe.”**

Lewis Carroll

Wisdom of the Week

Did your faces get sillier over the course of the week? Why or why not? Did they affect your overall mood?

Think of someone you admire who is a bit peculiar. What do you admire most about them?

8 SUNDAY

9 MONDAY

10 TUESDAY Peculiar People Day

11 WEDNESDAY

12 THURSDAY

13 FRIDAY

14 SATURDAY

Well-Being Check-In

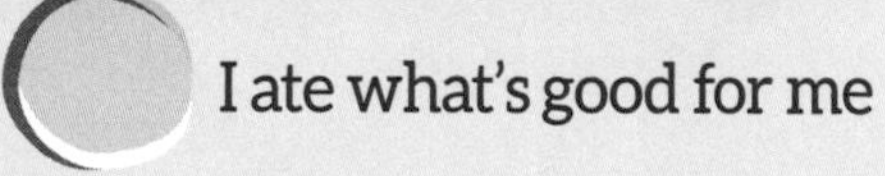

I kept my body moving   I ate what's good for me

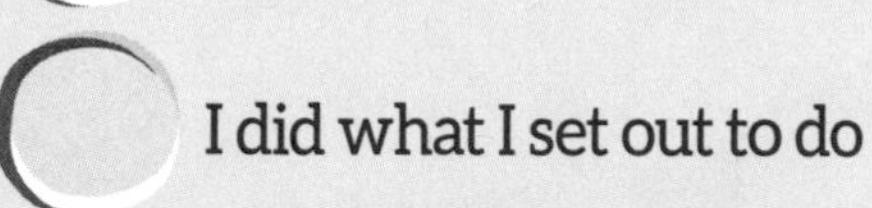

I connected with others   I did what I set out to do

S	M	T	W	T	F	S
1	2	3	4	5	6	7
8	9	10	11	12	13	14
15	16	17	18	19	20	21
22	23	24	25	26	27	28
29	30	31	1	2	3	4

Dare to dream.

What is your dream for the world?
Example: My dream is that no child ever goes to bed hungry.

What can you do this week to take at least one intentional action toward making your dream a reality?

"THE TIME IS ALWAYS RIGHT TO DO WHAT IS RIGHT."

MARTIN LUTHER KING JR.

Wisdom of the Week

Describe a specific way the world has become a better place for humankind during your lifetime.

15 SUNDAY

16 MONDAY Martin Luther King Jr. Day (U.S.)

17 TUESDAY

18 WEDNESDAY

19 THURSDAY

20 FRIDAY Inauguration Day (U.S.)

21 SATURDAY

Well-Being Check-In

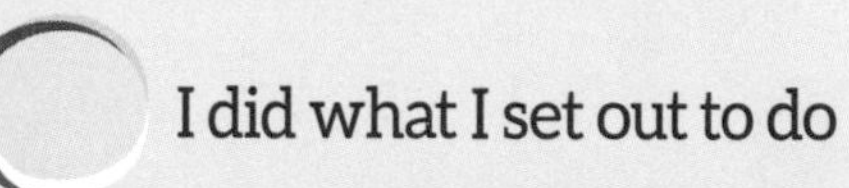

- I kept my body moving
- I ate what's good for me
- I connected with others
- I did what I set out to do

S	M	T	W	T	F	S
1	2	3	4	5	6	7
8	9	10	11	12	13	14
15	16	17	18	19	20	21
22	23	24	25	26	27	28
29	30	31	1	2	3	4

What if you began flinging compliments around with wild abandon?

See how many smiles and blushes you can create by giving a compliment to everyone you encounter this week – close friends, complete strangers and everyone in between. Write down your favorite ones in the spaces above.

“FLATTERY IS ALL RIGHT SO LONG AS YOU DON'T INHALE.”

ADLAI STEVENSON

Wisdom of the Week

Describe the most powerful compliment you gave this week.

As the week went on, did you find it easier to say nice things?

22 SUNDAY

23 MONDAY

24 TUESDAY Compliment Day

25 WEDNESDAY

26 THURSDAY

Atria Resident Appreciation Toast

27 FRIDAY

28 SATURDAY Chinese New Year

Well-Being Check-In

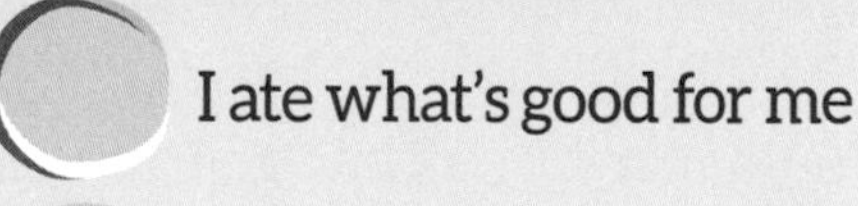

- I kept my body moving
- I ate what's good for me
- I connected with others
- I did what I set out to do

S	M	T	W	T	F	S
1	2	3	4	5	6	7
8	9	10	11	12	13	14
15	16	17	18	19	20	21
22	23	24	25	26	27	28
29	30	31	1	2	3	4

How well is your being?

Four fascinating weeks have flown by.

Before you charge full steam ahead into next month, take some time to focus your inquisitiveness inward – to your own well-being.

Sum up your four key lifestyle choices over the last four weeks. Look back at your smileys to jog your memory.

Nutrition

What I ate that was good for me

____

____

____

____

Goals

What I did that I set out to do

____

____

____

____

Exercise

How I kept my body moving

____

____

____

____

Connection

How I connected with others

____

____

____

____

My Magic Moment A time in the last month that made me happy or proud

____

What I learned

____

____

How I will grow from it

____

____

When I will do it

- [ ] now
- [ ] next week
- [ ] by the end of the month
- [ ] other ____________

Who I will ask to help me

____

Why they are qualified

____

____

Why my future self should be excited

____

____

Curiosity Catalyst

WHAT WOULD HAPPEN IF, AT THE EXACT SAME TIME, EVERYONE ON EARTH STOPPED TALKING FOR TWO WHOLE MINUTES?

What if instead of solving puzzles, you created one?

Sure, we all feel smart when we solve a puzzle. But have you ever tried to create one?

Give it a go in the space below. It can be any kind: crossword, sudoku, tangram, rebus, brainteaser or anything else you like. Then invite someone else to solve it.

“WHEN YOU HAVE EXHAUSTED ALL POSSIBILITIES, REMEMBER THIS – YOU HAVEN’T.”

THOMAS EDISON

Wisdom of the Week

Did you find it harder to create a puzzle than to solve one? In what way?

Many animals can learn to *solve* puzzles, but we have yet to find that any actually *create* them. Why do you think that is?

29 SUNDAY International Puzzle Day

30 MONDAY

31 TUESDAY

1 WEDNESDAY

2 THURSDAY Groundhog Day

3 FRIDAY

4 SATURDAY

Well-Being Check-In

I kept my body moving

I ate what’s good for me

I connected with others

I did what I set out to do

S	M	T	W	T	F	S
29	30	31	1	2	3	4
5	6	7	8	9	10	11
12	13	14	15	16	17	18
19	20	21	22	23	24	25
26	27	28	1	2	3	4

Can you turn a stranger into a friend?

When is the last time you made a new buddy? Approach someone you haven't spoken with before, throw caution to the wind and see if they have the makings of a new pal.

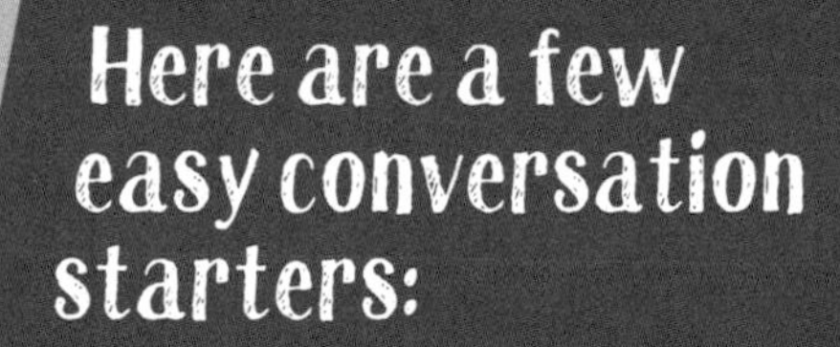

What's your favorite way to spend an afternoon?

Where's the most exotic place you've ever visited?

When you were a kid, what did you want to be when you grew up?

What's your favorite thing to eat?

Have you ever met one of your heroes?

"A STRANGER IS JUST A FRIEND I HAVEN'T MET YET."

WILL ROGERS

5 SUNDAY Super Bowl® LI

6 MONDAY

7 TUESDAY

8 WEDNESDAY

9 THURSDAY

10 FRIDAY Tu B'Shevat

11 SATURDAY Make a Friend Day

Wisdom of the Week

What's the most interesting thing you learned about your new friend?

What did you share with your new friend about yourself?

Well-Being Check-In

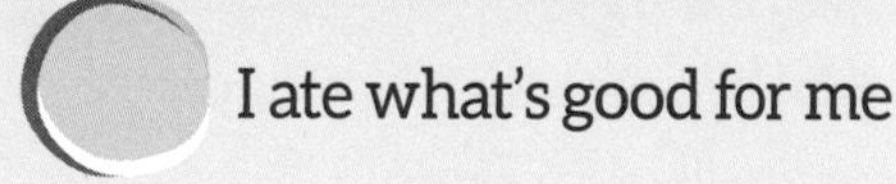

- I kept my body moving
- I ate what's good for me
- I connected with others
- I did what I set out to do

S	M	T	W	T	F	S
29	30	31	1	2	3	4
5	6	7	8	9	10	11
12	13	14	15	16	17	18
19	20	21	22	23	24	25
26	27	28	1	2	3	4

How many sizes can you grow your heart?

Here are three good ways to find out.

If you've let more than seven days go by without saying "I love you" to anyone you love, **DO IT NOW**.

Find something – anything – to love about someone you don't.

Challenge yourself to come up with a creative answer.

Commit a random act of kindness, enlisting the help of at least one accomplice.

Here are some ideas, or think of an even better one yourself.

- Hang a sign on a bulletin board that says "Take What You Need" with tear-off tabs at the bottom with the words "love," "hope," "cheer" and "courage."
- Put sticky notes with positive messages like "You look gorgeous" on a restroom mirror.
- Bring water, coffee or hot chocolate to outdoor workers like police officers or crossing guards.

"WHEN ALL YOUR DESIRES ARE DISTILLED; YOU WILL CAST JUST TWO VOTES: TO LOVE MORE, AND BE HAPPY."

HAFIZ OF PERSIA

12 SUNDAY

13 MONDAY

14 TUESDAY Valentine's Day

15 WEDNESDAY Flag Day (Canada)

16 THURSDAY

17 FRIDAY Random Acts of Kindness Day

18 SATURDAY

Wisdom of the Week

Did you learn anything new this week about your capacity for love? Describe.

Well-Being Check-In

- I kept my body moving
- I ate what's good for me
- I connected with others
- I did what I set out to do

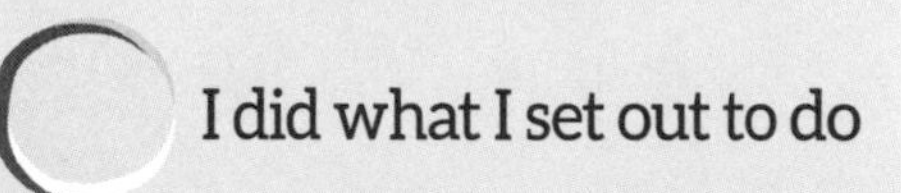

S	M	T	W	T	F	S
29	30	31	1	2	3	4
5	6	7	8	9	10	11
12	13	14	15	16	17	18
19	20	21	22	23	24	25
26	27	28	1	2	3	4

What if you were the leader of the country this week?

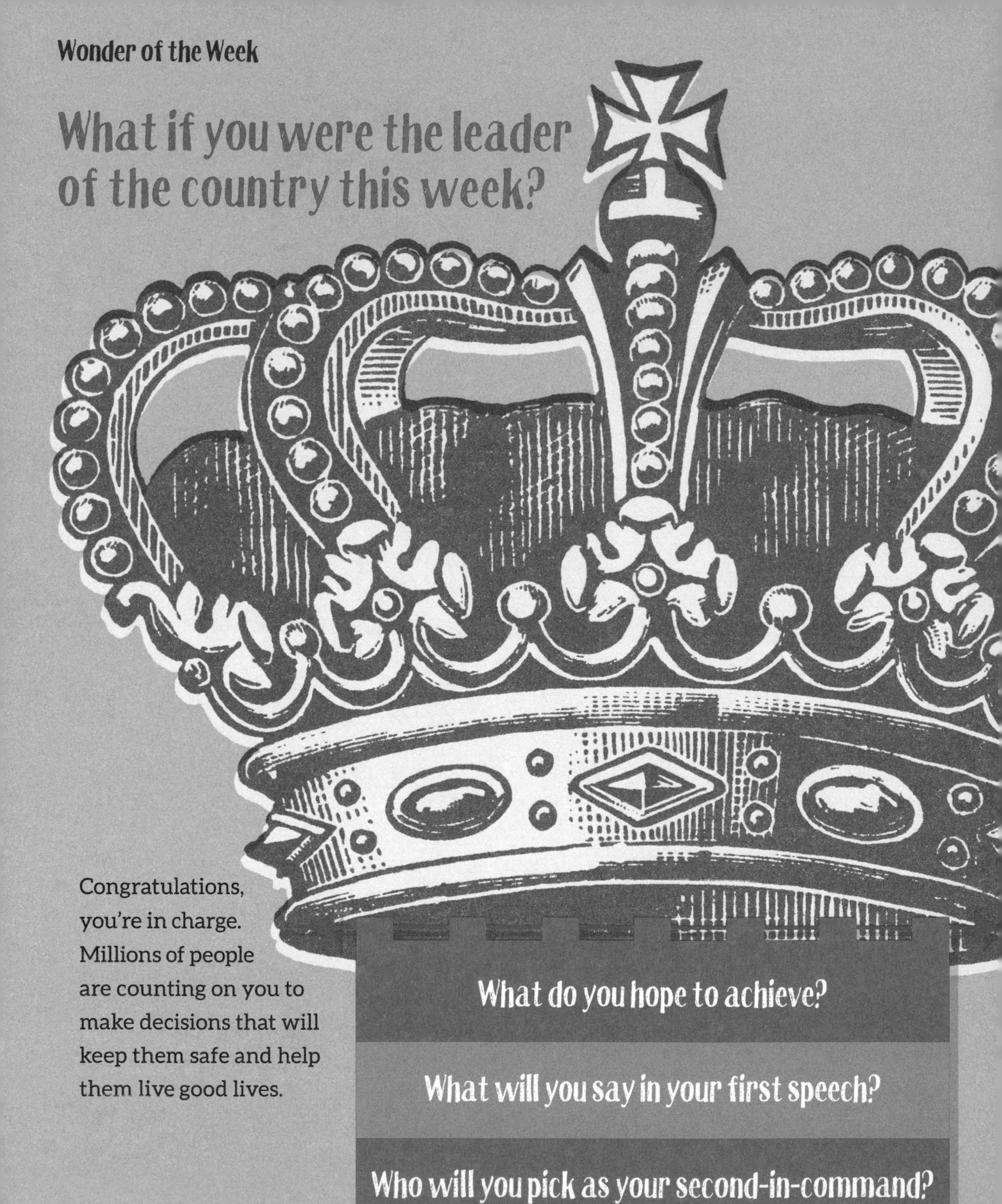

Congratulations, you're in charge. Millions of people are counting on you to make decisions that will keep them safe and help them live good lives.

What do you hope to achieve?

What will you say in your first speech?

Who will you pick as your second-in-command?

"LEADERSHIP AND LEARNING ARE INDISPENSABLE TO EACH OTHER."

JOHN F. KENNEDY

Wisdom of the Week

What are the qualities of a good leader?

____

____

Do you think those qualities improve with age? Yes No

What are the qualities of a good follower?

____

____

Do you think those qualities improve with age? Yes No

19 SUNDAY

20 MONDAY Presidents' Day (U.S.)

21 TUESDAY

22 WEDNESDAY

23 THURSDAY

24 FRIDAY

25 SATURDAY

Well-Being Check-In

I kept my body moving

I ate what's good for me

I connected with others

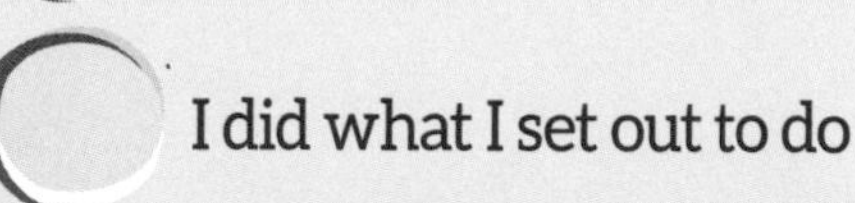

I did what I set out to do

S	M	T	W	T	F	S
29	30	31	1	2	3	4
5	6	7	8	9	10	11
12	13	14	15	16	17	18
19	20	21	22	23	24	25
26	27	28	1	2	3	4

How well is your being?

Four fascinating weeks have flown by.

Before you charge full steam ahead into next month, take some time to focus your inquisitiveness inward – to your own well-being.

Sum up your four key lifestyle choices over the last four weeks. Look back at your smileys to jog your memory.

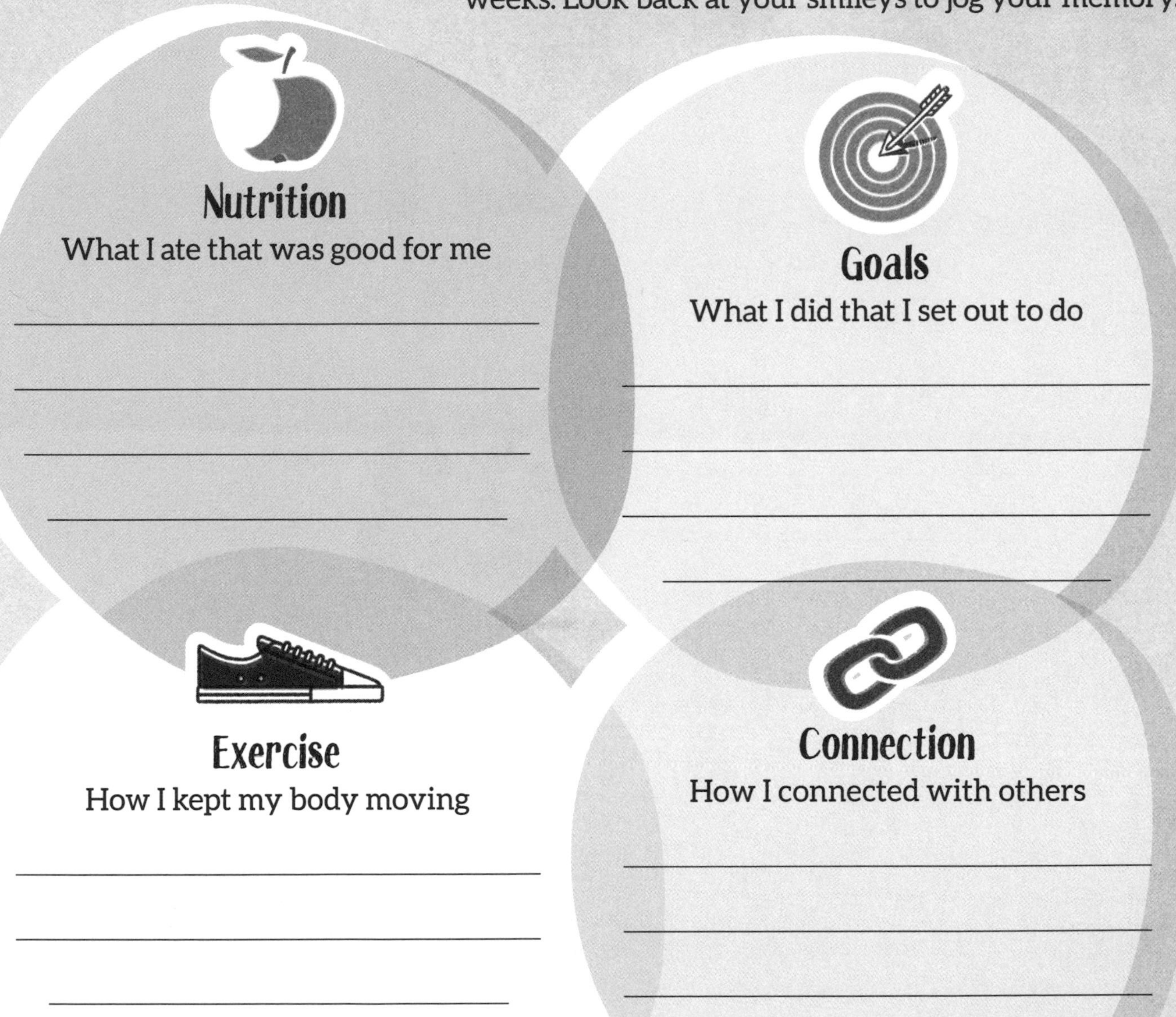

My Magic Moment A time in the last month that made me happy or proud

What I learned

How I will grow from it

When I will do it

- [ ] now
- [ ] next week
- [ ] by the end of the month
- [ ] other ____________

Who I will ask to help me

Why they are qualified

Why my future self should be excited

NOW PLAYING ______________________________

STARRING ______________________________ AS ME

COSTARRING ______________________ AS ______________________

ALSO COSTARRING ______________________ AS ______________________

DIRECTED BY ______________________________

GENRE ○ ADVENTURE ○ COMEDY ○ DRAMA ○ MUSICAL ○ THRILLER
○ SCI-FI ○ ACTION ○ WESTERN ○ ROMANCE ○ EPIC

“I AM BIG. IT’S THE PICTURES THAT GOT SMALL.”

GLORIA SWANSON
AS NORMA DESMOND
IN *SUNSET BOULEVARD*

Wisdom of the Week

The movie about your life so far is a blockbuster. What are your ideas for the sequel?

26 SUNDAY 89th Academy Awards®

27 MONDAY

28 TUESDAY Mardi Gras

1 WEDNESDAY Ash Wednesday

2 THURSDAY

3 FRIDAY

4 SATURDAY

Well-Being Check-In

I kept my body moving

I ate what’s good for me

I connected with others

I did what I set out to do

S	M	T	W	T	F	S
26	27	28	1	2	3	4
5	6	7	8	9	10	11
12	13	14	15	16	17	18
19	20	21	22	23	24	25
26	27	28	29	30	31	1

What if women had ruled the world throughout history?

There are many women leaders today, but what if they had always been in control?

How might history be different?

"IN POLITICS, IF YOU WANT ANYTHING SAID, ASK A MAN. IF YOU WANT ANYTHING DONE, ASK A WOMAN."

MARGARET THATCHER

Wisdom of the Week

Besides your mother, what woman has had the greatest influence in your life?

___

___

___

If you had a say in the matter before you were born, would you choose to be a man or a woman? Why?

___

___

___

___

5 SUNDAY

6 MONDAY

7 TUESDAY

8 WEDNESDAY International Women's Day

9 THURSDAY

10 FRIDAY

11 SATURDAY Purim

Well-Being Check-In

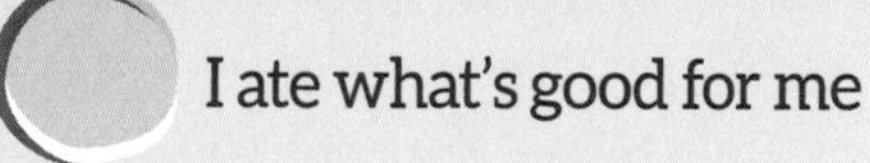

I kept my body moving

I ate what's good for me

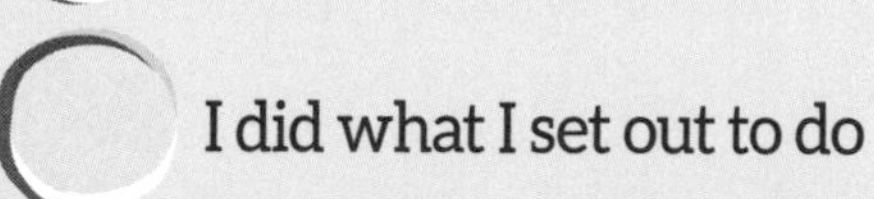

I connected with others

I did what I set out to do

S	M	T	W	T	F	S
26	27	28	1	2	3	4
5	6	7	8	9	10	11
12	13	14	15	16	17	18
19	20	21	22	23	24	25
26	27	28	29	30	31	1

Do you believe in luck?

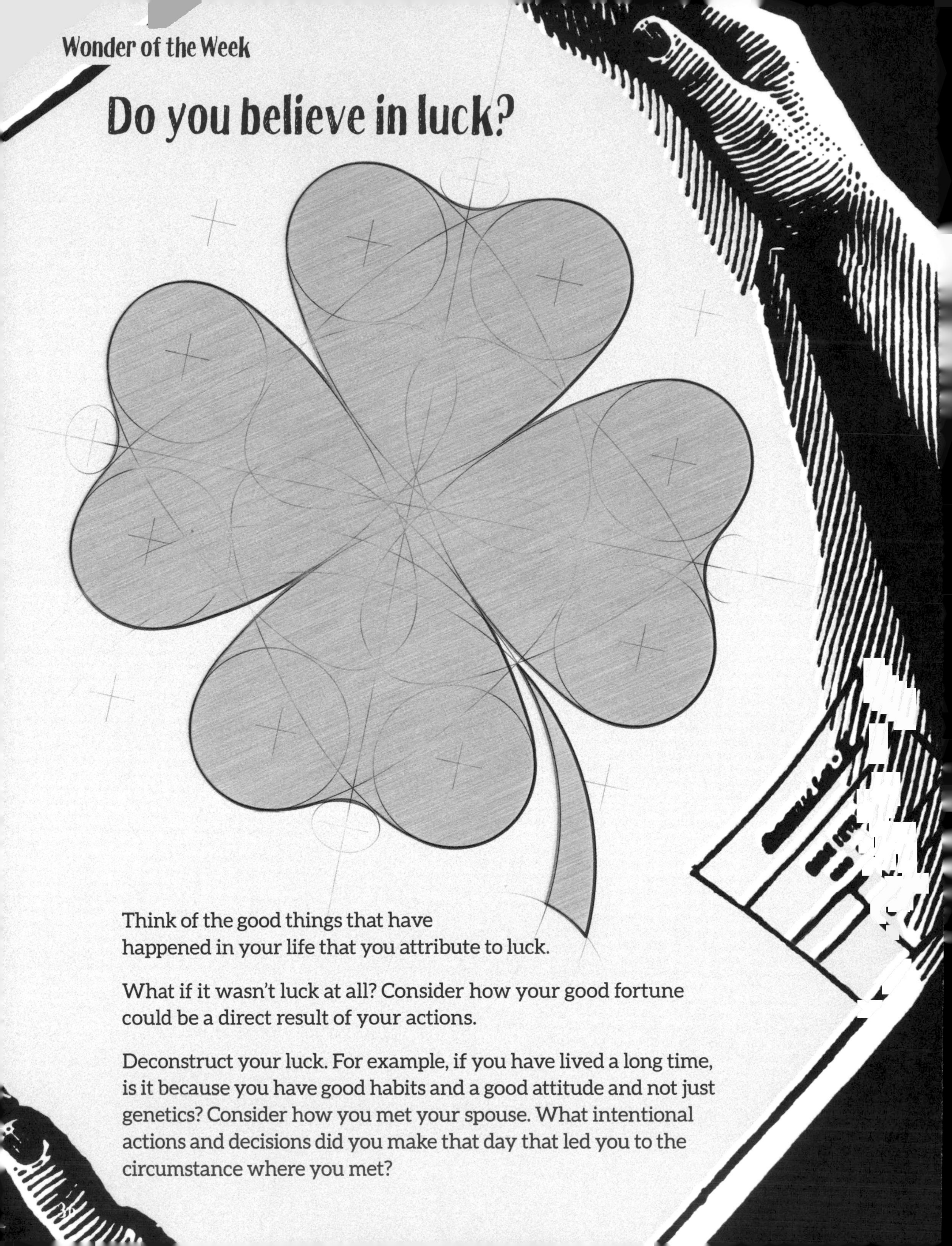

Think of the good things that have happened in your life that you attribute to luck.

What if it wasn't luck at all? Consider how your good fortune could be a direct result of your actions.

Deconstruct your luck. For example, if you have lived a long time, is it because you have good habits and a good attitude and not just genetics? Consider how you met your spouse. What intentional actions and decisions did you make that day that led you to the circumstance where you met?

"LUCK IS NOT CHANCE— IT'S TOIL— FORTUNE'S EXPENSIVE SMILE IS EARNED."

EMILY DICKINSON

12 SUNDAY Daylight Saving Time Begins

13 MONDAY

14 TUESDAY

15 WEDNESDAY

16 THURSDAY

17 FRIDAY St. Patrick's Day

18 SATURDAY

Wisdom of the Week

Do you consider yourself a lucky person or an unlucky person? Why?

Well-Being Check-In

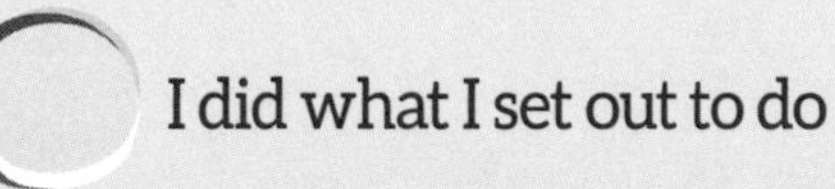

- I kept my body moving
- I ate what's good for me
- I connected with others
- I did what I set out to do

S	M	T	W	T	F	S
26	27	28	1	2	3	4
5	6	7	8	9	10	11
12	13	14	15	16	17	18
19	20	21	22	23	24	25
26	27	28	29	30	31	1

What if we wrote a story together?

Millions of stories have been told, and the number yet to be shared is infinite.

Keep the tradition going by gathering up to six friends in a circle. Complete the first sentence below yourself, then pass the book to your right. That person will complete the second sentence and pass the book to their right and so on, until you have made a fascinating new contribution to the library of humanity.

During a leisurely stroll one sunny morning, I was ____________________ to discover ____________________
(emotional reaction)

____.

That's when my neighbor, Betty, told me ____________

____.

I didn't know what to think because ______________

____.

Unfortunately, that's about the time ______________

____.

My friends and I talked it over and ______________

____.

Finally, I decided to ____________________________.

It was a/an ________________ day I won't soon forget.
(adjective)

- THE END

"Those who tell the stories rule the world."

Hopi proverb

Wisdom of the Week

Tell someone else a true story from your own life. Did you enjoy it more than creating a new story, or was it more difficult?

19 SUNDAY

20 MONDAY World Storytelling Day

21 TUESDAY

22 WEDNESDAY

23 THURSDAY

24 FRIDAY

25 SATURDAY

Well-Being Check-In

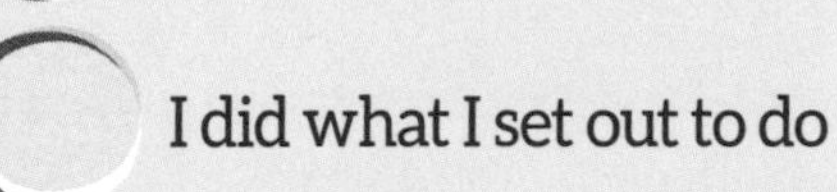

I kept my body moving

I ate what's good for me

I connected with others

I did what I set out to do

S	M	T	W	T	F	S
26	27	28	1	2	3	4
5	6	7	8	9	10	11
12	13	14	15	16	17	18
19	20	21	22	23	24	25
26	27	28	29	30	31	1

What if everybody were a comedian?

We're all funny in some way. This week, be especially aware of how you share your own particular sense of humor with the world.

For inspiration, consider that even some of the most famous comedians had other, decidedly less wacky, jobs at one time. Try to match these funny people with their pre-comedy profession.

Violinist

Accountant

Carnival Barker

Ice Cream Parlor Worker

Magician and Naval Officer

Drummer and Army Corporal

Homemaker and Copywriter

Movie Theater Usherette

Mel Brooks

Lucille Ball

Phyllis Diller

Jackie Gleason

Johnny Carson

Carol Burnett

Bob Newhart

Jack Benny

Answers: Violinist - Jack Benny; Accountant - Bob Newhart; Carnival Barker - Jackie Gleason; Ice Cream Parlor Worker - Lucille Ball; Magician and Naval Officer - Johnny Carson; Drummer and Army Corporal - Mel Brooks; Homemaker and Copywriter - Phyllis Diller; Movie Theater Usherette - Carol Burnett

"JESTERS DO OFT PROVE PROPHETS."

WILLIAM SHAKESPEARE

26 SUNDAY

27 MONDAY

28 TUESDAY

29 WEDNESDAY

30 THURSDAY

31 FRIDAY

1 SATURDAY April Fools' Day

Wisdom of the Week

Would you rather play a prank or be pranked?

What is the best prank anyone has ever played on you?

Well-Being Check-In

I kept my body moving

I ate what's good for me

I connected with others

I did what I set out to do

S	M	T	W	T	F	S
26	27	28	1	2	3	4
5	6	7	8	9	10	11
12	13	14	15	16	17	18
19	20	21	22	23	24	25
26	27	28	29	30	31	1

How well is your being?

Five fascinating weeks have flown by.

Before you charge full steam ahead into next month, take some time to focus your inquisitiveness inward – to your own well-being.

Sum up your four key lifestyle choices over the last five weeks. Look back at your smileys to jog your memory.

Nutrition

What I ate that was good for me

Goals

What I did that I set out to do

Exercise

How I kept my body moving

Connection

How I connected with others

My Magic Moment A time in the last month that made me happy or proud

What I learned

____

____

How I will grow from it

____

____

When I will do it

- ☐ now
- ☐ next week
- ☐ by the end of the month
- ☐ other ____________

Who I will ask to help me

____

Why they are qualified

____

____

Why my future self should be excited

____

____

Curiosity Catalyst **WHAT IF YOU ASKED TWO QUESTIONS FOR EVERY STATEMENT YOU MADE?**

What if you could make up a holiday?

This coming Friday will be a holiday of your invention.

Think about a person, thing or idea that has no holiday dedicated to celebrating it and – to your thinking – truly deserves one. Give your holiday a name and write it on the calendar.

"EVERY DAY IS A GOOD DAY. THERE IS SOMETHING TO LEARN, CARE ABOUT AND CELEBRATE."

AMIT RAY

2 SUNDAY

3 MONDAY

4 TUESDAY

5 WEDNESDAY

6 THURSDAY

7 FRIDAY My Holiday

8 SATURDAY

Wisdom of the Week

Do you think there are already too many holidays? Or are there not enough? Explain.

Well-Being Check-In

I kept my body moving

I ate what's good for me

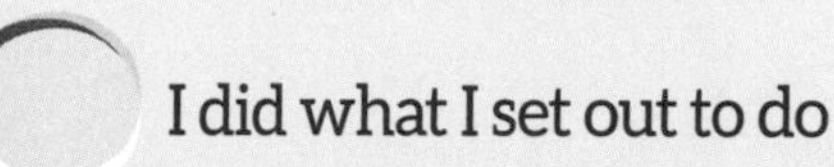

I connected with others

I did what I set out to do

S	M	T	W	T	F	S
26	27	28	29	30	31	1
2	3	4	5	6	7	8
9	10	11	12	13	14	15
16	17	18	19	20	21	22
23	24	25	26	27	28	29
30	1	2	3	4	5	6

What if you renewed yourself the way nature does?

It's spring. The flowers and trees are budding. The sun is shining a little longer.

What can you do – physically, spiritually and emotionally – to renew yourself and be a vital participant in the wonder of spring? Go outside and get inspired.

“Live in each season as it passes; breathe the air, drink the drink, taste the fruit, and resign yourself to the influence of the Earth.”

Henry David Thoreau

Wisdom of the Week

Think about a hardship you endured that resulted in something good afterward. If you could go back, would you change the way things happened? How?

If it were always spring, would it still be as beautiful?

---

9 SUNDAY Palm Sunday

10 MONDAY Passover Begins

11 TUESDAY

12 WEDNESDAY

13 THURSDAY

14 FRIDAY Good Friday

15 SATURDAY

Well-Being Check-In

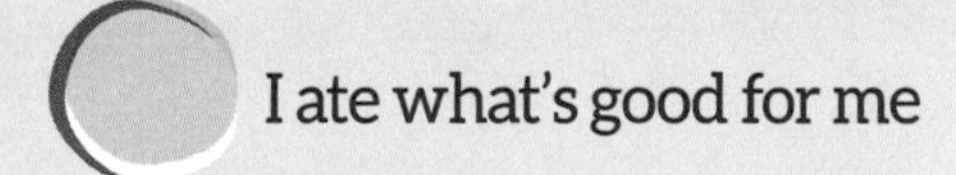

I kept my body moving — I ate what's good for me

I connected with others — I did what I set out to do

S	M	T	W	T	F	S
26	27	28	29	30	31	1
2	3	4	5	6	7	8
9	10	11	12	13	14	15
16	17	18	19	20	21	22
23	24	25	26	27	28	29
30	1	2	3	4	5	6

How will you spoil your great-great-great-great-grandchildren?

You can start by giving them a healthy planet.

Imagine it's the year 2117. Children all over the world are playing, growing and thriving.

What will they learn in school about what you did during your time on Earth to help leave them a safe, clean environment?

"HERE IS YOUR COUNTRY. CHERISH THESE NATURAL WONDERS, CHERISH THE NATURAL RESOURCES, CHERISH THE HISTORY AND ROMANCE AS A SACRED HERITAGE, FOR YOUR CHILDREN AND YOUR CHILDREN'S CHILDREN."

THEODORE ROOSEVELT

Wisdom of the Week

What natural feature of our planet do you find the most beautiful or fascinating? Why?

16 SUNDAY Easter

17 MONDAY

18 TUESDAY Passover Ends

19 WEDNESDAY

20 THURSDAY

21 FRIDAY

22 SATURDAY Earth Day

Well-Being Check-In

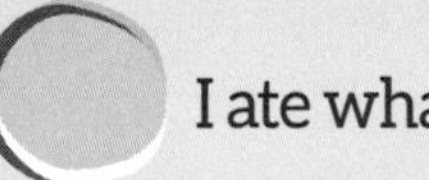

I kept my body moving

I ate what's good for me

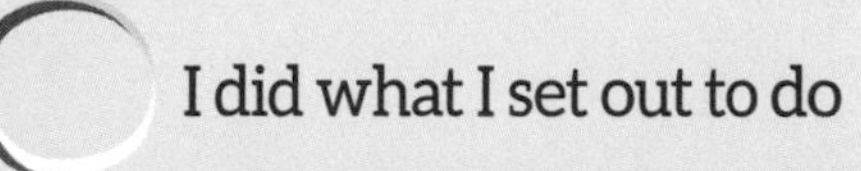

I connected with others

I did what I set out to do

S	M	T	W	T	F	S
26	27	28	29	30	31	1
2	3	4	5	6	7	8
9	10	11	12	13	14	15
16	17	18	19	20	21	22
23	24	25	26	27	28	29
30	1	2	3	4	5	6

How does our capacity for faith guide our lives?

This week, explore how faith influences your life and well-being.

Whether it is in a person, an idea or a higher power, the ability to believe in what we cannot know for sure is a uniquely human quality. Faith simultaneously makes us stronger and more vulnerable. It is equally capable of creating both the most fulfilling and the most devastating moments of our lives.

Think about a time when faith gave you strength in the face of adversity.

Now think about a time when you had faith in someone or something and they let you down. Do you regret it, or do you still believe it's better to have faith than not?

"FAITH IS A KNOWLEDGE WITHIN THE HEART, BEYOND THE REACH OF PROOF."

KHALIL GIBRAN

23 SUNDAY Holocaust Remembrance Day

24 MONDAY

25 TUESDAY

26 WEDNESDAY

27 THURSDAY

28 FRIDAY Arbor Day (U.S.)

29 SATURDAY

Wisdom of the Week

What insights have you gained about faith this week?

Has your capacity for faith grown or diminished over the years?

Well-Being Check-In

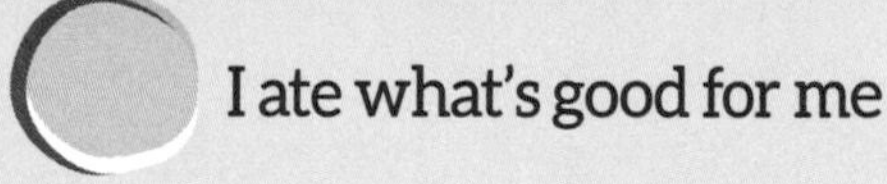

I kept my body moving

I ate what's good for me

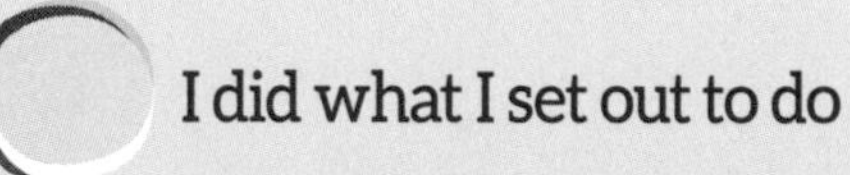

I connected with others

I did what I set out to do

S	M	T	W	T	F	S
26	27	28	29	30	31	1
2	3	4	5	6	7	8
9	10	11	12	13	14	15
16	17	18	19	20	21	22
23	24	25	26	27	28	29
30	1	2	3	4	5	6

How well is your being?

Four fascinating weeks have flown by.

Before you charge full steam ahead into next month, take some time to focus your inquisitiveness inward – to your own well-being.

Sum up your four key lifestyle choices over the last four weeks. Look back at your smileys to jog your memory.

My Magic Moment A time in the last month that made me happy or proud

What I learned

____

____

How I will grow from it

____

____

When I will do it

- [ ] now
- [ ] next week
- [ ] by the end of the month
- [ ] other ______________

Who I will ask to help me

____

Why they are qualified

____

____

Why my future self should be excited

____

____

Curiosity Catalyst

CONSIDER THE POSSIBILITY THAT YOUR FAVORITE HUMAN BEING ON THE PLANET IS THINKING OF YOU RIGHT NOW.

When was the last time you learned something for the first time?

Growing up, the classroom was full of subjects we *had* to learn. Now we have the freedom to study what we *want* to learn. What was the first thing you studied on your own purely because it interested you? Who helped you learn it?

"WE ARE ALL FAILURES – AT LEAST THE BEST OF US ARE."

J.M. BARRIE

Wisdom of the Week

What's the next thing you'd like to learn?

Whether inside or outside the classroom, did you have a favorite teacher growing up? What made them so memorable?

30 SUNDAY

1 MONDAY

2 TUESDAY Teachers' Day (U.S.)

3 WEDNESDAY

4 THURSDAY

5 FRIDAY Cinco de Mayo

6 SATURDAY

Well-Being Check-In

I kept my body moving

I ate what's good for me

I connected with others

I did what I set out to do

S	M	T	W	T	F	S
30	1	2	3	4	5	6
7	8	9	10	11	12	13
14	15	16	17	18	19	20
21	22	23	24	25	26	27
28	29	30	31	1	2	3

Try giving a caring person a dose of their own medicine.

As one of the noblest traits, compassion can be the most heartfelt expression of love.

In the space below, write about a time when someone showed compassion for you when you needed it most.

____

____

____

____

Carry this feeling in your heart this week, and let it inspire your own expressions of compassion toward a caregiver, neighbor or anyone who shows compassion to you or others. These opportunities often arise unexpectedly, so with open eyes and an intentional heart, be ready to act when someone needs a supportive gesture.

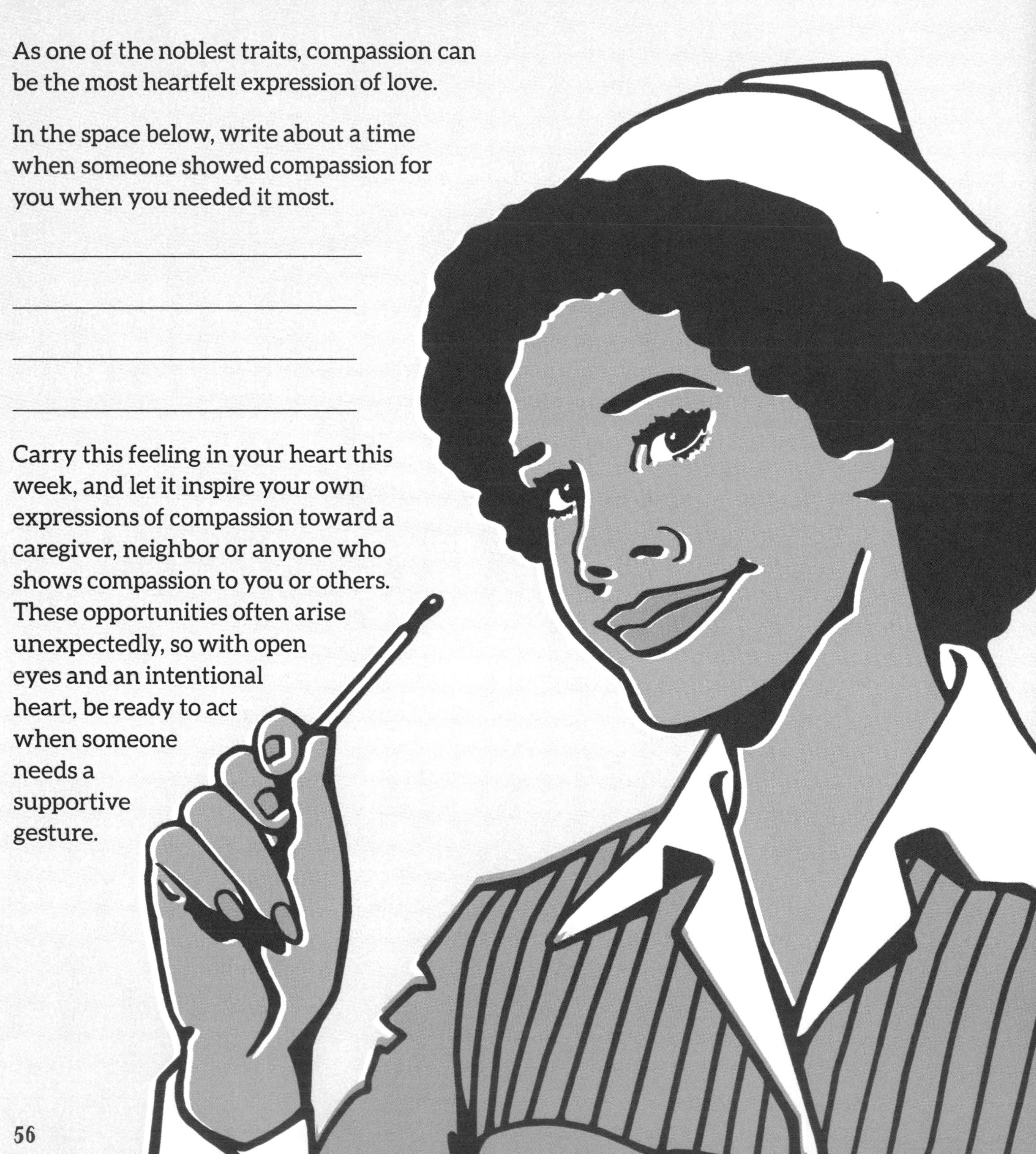

"LOVE AND COMPASSION ARE NECESSITIES, NOT LUXURIES. WITHOUT THEM, HUMANITY CANNOT SURVIVE."

TENZIN GYATSO, THE 14TH DALAI LAMA

7 SUNDAY Nurses Week

8 MONDAY

9 TUESDAY

10 WEDNESDAY

11 THURSDAY

12 FRIDAY International Nurses Day

13 SATURDAY

Wisdom of the Week

How did it feel to show compassion?
How did the recipient respond?

Well-Being Check-In

I kept my body moving

I ate what's good for me

I connected with others

I did what I set out to do

S	M	T	W	T	F	S
30	1	2	3	4	5	6
7	8	9	10	11	12	13
14	15	16	17	18	19	20
21	22	23	24	25	26	27
28	29	30	31	1	2	3

What would Mom do?

Mom always knew what to do. Whether you crashed your tricycle trying to ride down the front steps, gave yourself an ill-advised haircut or put off doing a school project till the last minute, Mom was there to figure it out, clean up the mess and somehow make it all right – and make sure you learned how to do better next time.

This week, as often as possible, ask what your mom would have done. Solve a problem the way she would have. Use one of her catchphrases. Do a household task the way she would, even if it's not how you do it now. Eat her favorite food. Tell one of her favorite stories to someone who didn't know her.

"MOST MOTHERS ARE INSTINCTIVE PHILOSOPHERS."

HARRIET BEECHER STOWE

Wisdom of the Week

Did you gain any insights about your mother this week?

____

____

____

Do you think it's easier or harder to be a mom today than it was in your mother's time? Explain.

____

____

____

14 SUNDAY Mother's Day

15 MONDAY

16 TUESDAY

17 WEDNESDAY

18 THURSDAY

19 FRIDAY

20 SATURDAY Armed Forces Day (U.S.)

Well-Being Check-In

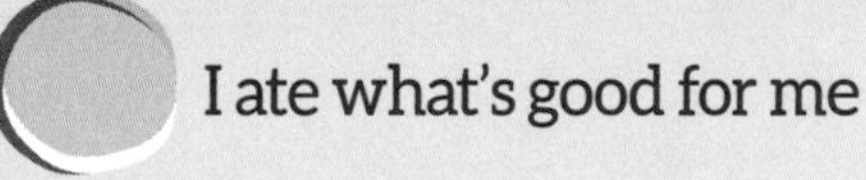

- I kept my body moving
- I ate what's good for me
- I connected with others
- I did what I set out to do

S	M	T	W	T	F	S
30	1	2	3	4	5	6
7	8	9	10	11	12	13
14	15	16	17	18	19	20
21	22	23	24	25	26	27
28	29	30	31	1	2	3

Dare to be a supersleuth.

It's easy to overlook things during our everyday routines. But paying attention helps us keep a sense of wonder about the world, no matter where we are. Here are a few things to look for this week to help you do just that.

1 Find someone who has visited more than five countries

____

2 Find something that gets overlooked

____

3 Find a beautiful shade of red

____

4 Find something that jingles

____

5 Find someone who can speak another language

____

6 Find someone who loves math

____

7 Find someone who shares your birthday

____

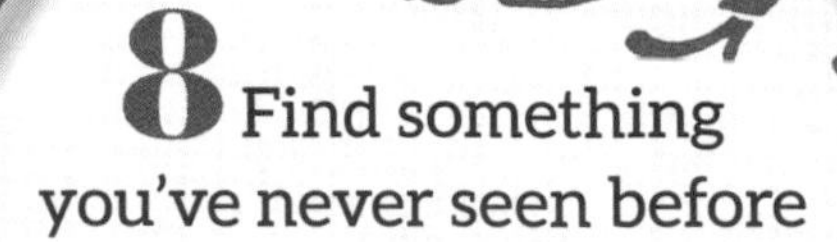

8 Find something you've never seen before

____

9 Find something that's just out of reach

____

10 Find a smell that reminds you of childhood

____

"THE MAIN THING IS TO CARE. CARE VERY HARD, EVEN IF IT IS ONLY A GAME YOU ARE PLAYING."

BILLIE JEAN KING

21 SUNDAY

22 MONDAY Victoria Day (Canada)

23 TUESDAY

24 WEDNESDAY Scavenger Hunt Day

25 THURSDAY

26 FRIDAY

27 SATURDAY

Wisdom of the Week

Did you find something interesting that was not on the list? Describe.

Well-Being Check-In

I kept my body moving

I ate what's good for me

I connected with others

I did what I set out to do

S	M	T	W	T	F	S
30	1	2	3	4	5	6
7	8	9	10	11	12	13
14	15	16	17	18	19	20
21	22	23	24	25	26	27
28	29	30	31	1	2	3

How can doing without do you good?

Choose something you enjoy – a favorite food, hobby or personal delight – and purposely not partake this week. Every time you think about – or almost indulge in – what you gave up, take a moment and appreciate the gift of sacrifice.

"THERE IS NO LIBERTY, SAVE WISDOM AND SELF-CONTROL. LIBERTY IS WITHIN – NOT WITHOUT. IT IS EACH MAN'S OWN AFFAIR."

H.G. WELLS

Wisdom of the Week

Now that your week of sacrifice has come to a close, do you think you will have a new appreciation for what you gave up?

What does sacrifice mean to you?

28 SUNDAY

29 MONDAY Memorial Day (U.S.)

30 TUESDAY Shavuot Begins

31 WEDNESDAY

1 THURSDAY Shavuot Ends

2 FRIDAY

3 SATURDAY

Well-Being Check-In

I kept my body moving

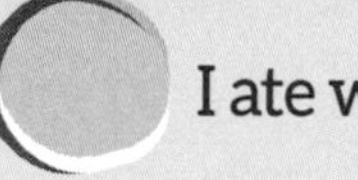

I ate what's good for me

I connected with others

I did what I set out to do

S	M	T	W	T	F	S
30	1	2	3	4	5	6
7	8	9	10	11	12	13
14	15	16	17	18	19	20
21	22	23	24	25	26	27
28	29	30	31	1	2	3

How well is your being?

Five fascinating weeks have flown by.

Before you charge full steam ahead into next month, take some time to focus your inquisitiveness inward – to your own well-being.

Sum up your four key lifestyle choices over the last five weeks. Look back at your smileys to jog your memory.

Nutrition

What I ate that was good for me

Goals

What I did that I set out to do

Exercise

How I kept my body moving

Connection

How I connected with others

My Magic Moment A time in the last month that made me happy or proud

What I learned

____

____

How I will grow from it

____

____

When I will do it

- [ ] now
- [ ] next week
- [ ] by the end of the month
- [ ] other ______________

Who I will ask to help me

____

Why they are qualified

____

____

Why my future self should be excited

____

____

Curiosity Catalyst

WHAT IF YOU KNEW YOU WERE GUARANTEED TO LIVE TO BE 150?

What if you could travel to *whenever* you wanted?

You have access to a time machine that can take you to any time and place in all of the past or future. The machine has enough fuel for one round-trip. When and where do you go?

____

____

____

____

Why did you pick that destination? What do you hope to experience?

____

____

____

____

____

"THE REAL VOYAGE OF DISCOVERY CONSISTS NOT IN SEEKING NEW LANDSCAPES, BUT IN HAVING NEW EYES."

MARCEL PROUST

Wisdom of the Week

When you daydream, do you find yourself looking back onto things of the past or considering that which has yet to occur? Why?

SUNDAY Canadian Armed Forces Day

5 **MONDAY**

6 **TUESDAY** D-Day (U.S.)

7 **WEDNESDAY**

8 **THURSDAY**

9 **FRIDAY**

10 **SATURDAY**

Well-Being Check-In

I kept my body moving

I ate what's good for me

I connected with others

I did what I set out to do

S	M	T	W	T	F	S
28	29	30	31	1	2	3
4	5	6	7	8	9	10
11	12	13	14	15	16	17
18	19	20	21	22	23	24
25	26	27	28	29	30	1

Let your ME flag fly.

Think about the qualities that make you the unique individual you are.

With those things in mind, design your own unique, personal flag.

What color represents your personality?

What shapes convey what you are passionate about?

What images symbolize what you stand for?

"ALWAYS BE A FIRST-RATE VERSION OF YOURSELF INSTEAD OF A SECOND-RATE VERSION OF SOMEBODY ELSE."

JUDY GARLAND

11 SUNDAY

12 MONDAY

13 TUESDAY

14 WEDNESDAY Flag Day (U.S.)

15 THURSDAY

16 FRIDAY

17 SATURDAY

Wisdom of the Week

If you had designed your own flag when you were much younger, what would be different? What would be the same?

Well-Being Check-In

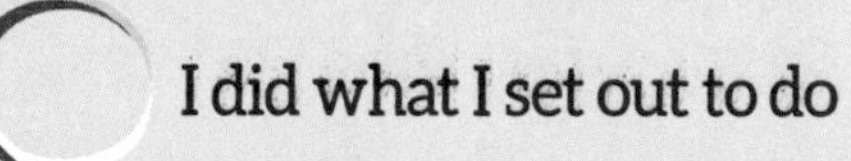

- I kept my body moving
- I ate what's good for me
- I connected with others
- I did what I set out to do

S	M	T	W	T	F	S
28	29	30	31	1	2	3
4	5	6	7	8	9	10
11	12	13	14	15	16	17
18	19	20	21	22	23	24
25	26	27	28	29	30	1

What lies beneath Dad's dad-ness?

Dads play a lot of roles in their children's lives: protector, provider, handyman and teacher, to name a few. But what do you know about the man behind the dad, the stuff that wasn't about being a parent? Even if you never knew him personally, you likely learned things about him from others.

Here are some questions to get you thinking.

What was his childhood like?

What was his favorite color?

What kind of music did he listen to?

Was he a man of his time,
or ahead of his time?

Would he think the world is better,
worse or just different today than
when he was young?

"One father is more than a hundred schoolmasters."

George Herbert

18 SUNDAY Father's Day

19 MONDAY

20 TUESDAY

21 WEDNESDAY

22 THURSDAY

23 FRIDAY

24 SATURDAY

Wisdom of the Week

Describe how your feelings about your father have changed over the years.

Well-Being Check-In

I kept my body moving

I ate what's good for me

I connected with others

I did what I set out to do

S	M	T	W	T	F	S
28	29	30	31	1	2	3
4	5	6	7	8	9	10
11	12	13	14	15	16	17
18	19	20	21	22	23	24
25	26	27	28	29	30	1

What if you didn't hide your hidden talent?

The stage is set for a pleasantly peculiar talent show and you're the next act. How will you "wow" the crowd? Everyone has a fun, hidden talent – wiggling their ears, curling their tongue or balancing a spoon on their nose, for example. What's yours?

Have fun this week reacquainting yourself with – or discovering – your special talent.

Share it with at least five people and ask about theirs, too.

“A really great talent finds its happiness in execution.”

Johann Wolfgang von Goethe

Wisdom of the Week

What’s one of your unique talents? Did you always know how to do it or was it something you learned?

How did it feel to share your talent?

25 SUNDAY

26 MONDAY

27 TUESDAY

28 WEDNESDAY

29 THURSDAY

30 FRIDAY

1 SATURDAY Canada Day

Well-Being Check-In

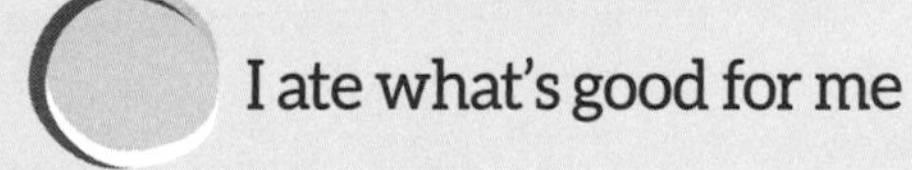

I kept my body moving

I ate what’s good for me

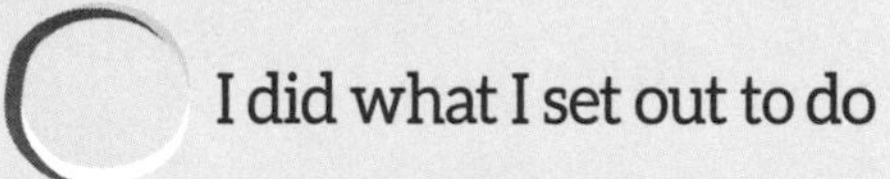

I connected with others

I did what I set out to do

S	M	T	W	T	F	S
28	29	30	31	1	2	3
4	5	6	7	8	9	10
11	12	13	14	15	16	17
18	19	20	21	22	23	24
25	26	27	28	29	30	1

How well is your being?

Four fascinating weeks have flown by.

Before you charge full steam ahead into next month, take some time to focus your inquisitiveness inward – to your own well-being.

Sum up your four key lifestyle choices over the last four weeks. Look back at your smileys to jog your memory.

Nutrition

What I ate that was good for me

Goals

What I did that I set out to do

Exercise

How I kept my body moving

Connection

How I connected with others

My Magic Moment A time in the last month that made me happy or proud

What I learned

____

____

How I will grow from it

____

____

When I will do it

- ☐ now
- ☐ next week
- ☐ by the end of the month
- ☐ other ____________

Who I will ask to help me

____

Why they are qualified

____

____

Why my future self should be excited

____

____

Curiosity Catalyst **WHAT IF YOU SUDDENLY HAD COMPLETE MASTERY OF ALL LANGUAGES?**

What do we do with our freedom?

Freedom is something we all desire and cherish,
yet what it means to each of us is highly subjective.
Why is a concept so universally valued so disparately defined?

Consider this: If a wolf gets his paw caught in a trap,
why does he try to escape? It's likely not because he consciously
desires freedom for its own sake, but because he's being prevented
from hunting and finding water, or he senses imminent danger.

With that in mind, think about freedom
in terms of the actions it allows.
What does freedom mean to a prisoner?
A teenager? A refugee?
What does it mean to you?

"I DIDN'T KNOW I WAS A SLAVE UNTIL I FOUND OUT I COULDN'T DO THE THINGS I WANTED."

FREDERICK DOUGLASS

SUNDAY

3 MONDAY

4 TUESDAY Independence Day (U.S.)

5 WEDNESDAY

6 THURSDAY

7 FRIDAY

8 SATURDAY

Wisdom of the Week

Is there any specific taste, smell, sight, sound or other experience that causes you to be most acutely aware and appreciative of your freedom? Explain.

Well-Being Check-In

I kept my body moving

I ate what's good for me

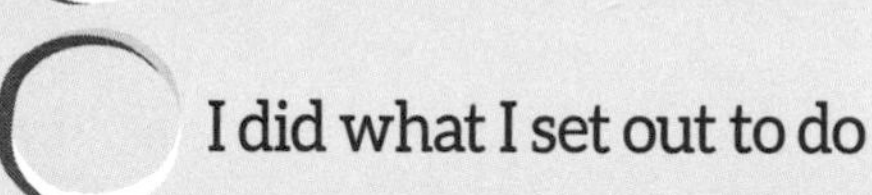

I connected with others

I did what I set out to do

S	M	T	W	T	F	S
25	26	27	28	29	30	1
2	3	4	5	6	7	8
9	10	11	12	13	14	15
16	17	18	19	20	21	22
23	24	25	26	27	28	29
30	31	1	2	3	4	5

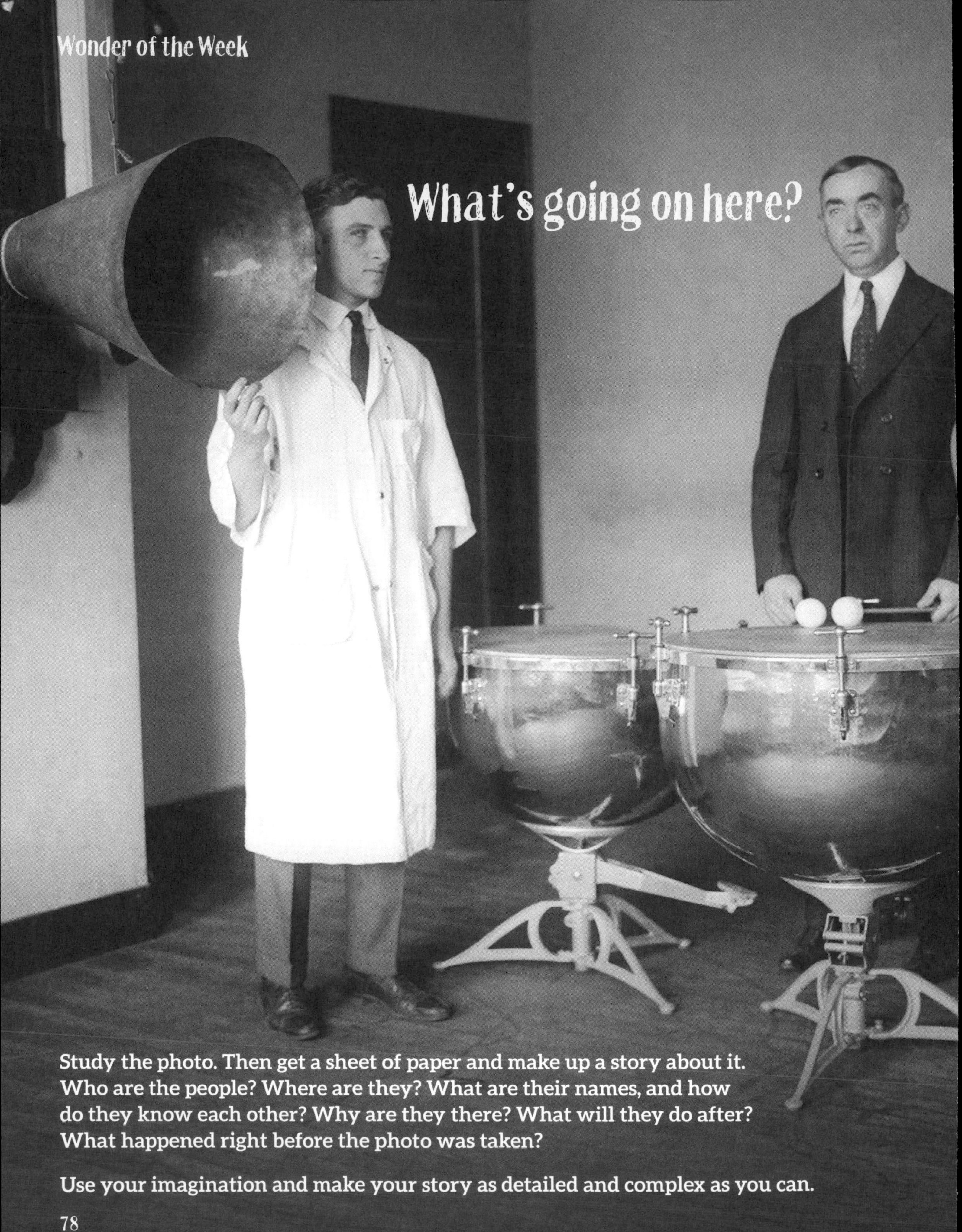

What's going on here?

Study the photo. Then get a sheet of paper and make up a story about it. Who are the people? Where are they? What are their names, and how do they know each other? Why are they there? What will they do after? What happened right before the photo was taken?

Use your imagination and make your story as detailed and complex as you can.

"YOU CAN'T DEPEND ON YOUR EYES WHEN YOUR IMAGINATION IS OUT OF FOCUS."

MARK TWAIN

Wisdom of the Week

Our imagination isn't just for fun. Write about how you used your imagination in a real-life situation this week.

9 SUNDAY

10 MONDAY

11 TUESDAY

12 WEDNESDAY

13 THURSDAY

14 FRIDAY

15 SATURDAY

Well-Being Check-In

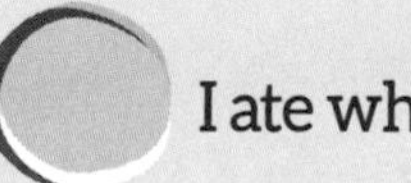

I kept my body moving

I ate what's good for me

I connected with others

I did what I set out to do

S	M	T	W	T	F	S
25	26	27	28	29	30	1
2	3	4	5	6	7	8
9	10	11	12	13	14	15
16	17	18	19	20	21	22
23	24	25	26	27	28	29
30	31	1	2	3	4	5

See if you can be the best listener in the room – without using your ears.

Listening is so much more than hearing. It's about being present in the moment and attentive to nonverbal cues.

Practice listening without your ears by writing down which emotion you think the people below are feeling based on their facial expressions. Then, the next time you see two people having a conversation, see what you can understand just by paying attention to facial expressions and body language.

"The word 'listen' contains the same letters as the word 'silent'."

Alfred Brendel

Wisdom of the Week

Listen to your memories to answer the following:

A sound that scares me ______________

A sound that comforts me ______________

A sound that excites me ______________

A sound that irritates me ______________

A sound I miss ______________

A sound I'll always remember ______________

16 SUNDAY

17 MONDAY

18 TUESDAY World Listening Day

19 WEDNESDAY

20 THURSDAY

21 FRIDAY

22 SATURDAY

Well-Being Check-In

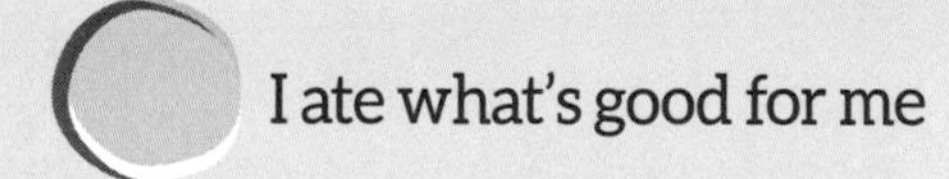
I kept my body moving

I ate what's good for me

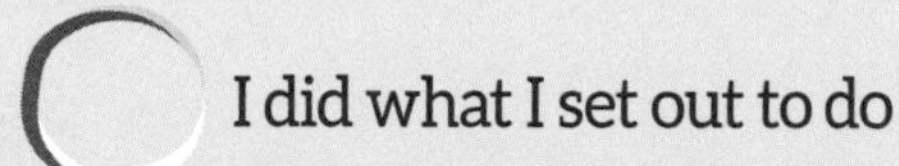
I connected with others

I did what I set out to do

S	M	T	W	T	F	S
25	26	27	28	29	30	1
2	3	4	5	6	7	8
9	10	11	12	13	14	15
16	17	18	19	20	21	22
23	24	25	26	27	28	29
30	31	1	2	3	4	5

What if you stopped and savored this week?

We need food to sustain us, of course. But how often do you take time to appreciate what an enriching part of life food can be? Eating is a delightful sensory experience. This week, focus on really tasting your food.

Start with a piece of fruit, a handful of nuts or a piece of cheese. Take a bite, close your eyes and concentrate on its aroma and flavor. Chewing slowly, note its texture and temperature. Savor the flavors on your tongue before swallowing. As you swallow, pay attention to any lingering sensations or aftertastes.

Write down what you ate and what you experienced.

"One cannot think well, love well, sleep well, if one has not dined well."

Virginia Woolf

Wisdom of the Week

Did savoring your food change what you ate this week? If so, how?

What types of flavors do you tend to enjoy - spicy, sweet, bitter, salty, sour? Why? Has your taste palate changed over the years? How?

23 SUNDAY

24 MONDAY

25 TUESDAY

26 WEDNESDAY

27 THURSDAY

28 FRIDAY

29 SATURDAY

Well-Being Check-In

I kept my body moving

I ate what's good for me

I connected with others

I did what I set out to do

S	M	T	W	T	F	S
25	26	27	28	29	30	1
2	3	4	5	6	7	8
9	10	11	12	13	14	15
16	17	18	19	20	21	22
23	24	25	26	27	28	29
30	31	1	2	3	4	5

How well is your being?

Four fascinating weeks have flown by.

Before you charge full steam ahead into next month, take some time to focus your inquisitiveness inward – to your own well-being.

Sum up your four key lifestyle choices over the last four weeks. Look back at your smileys to jog your memory.

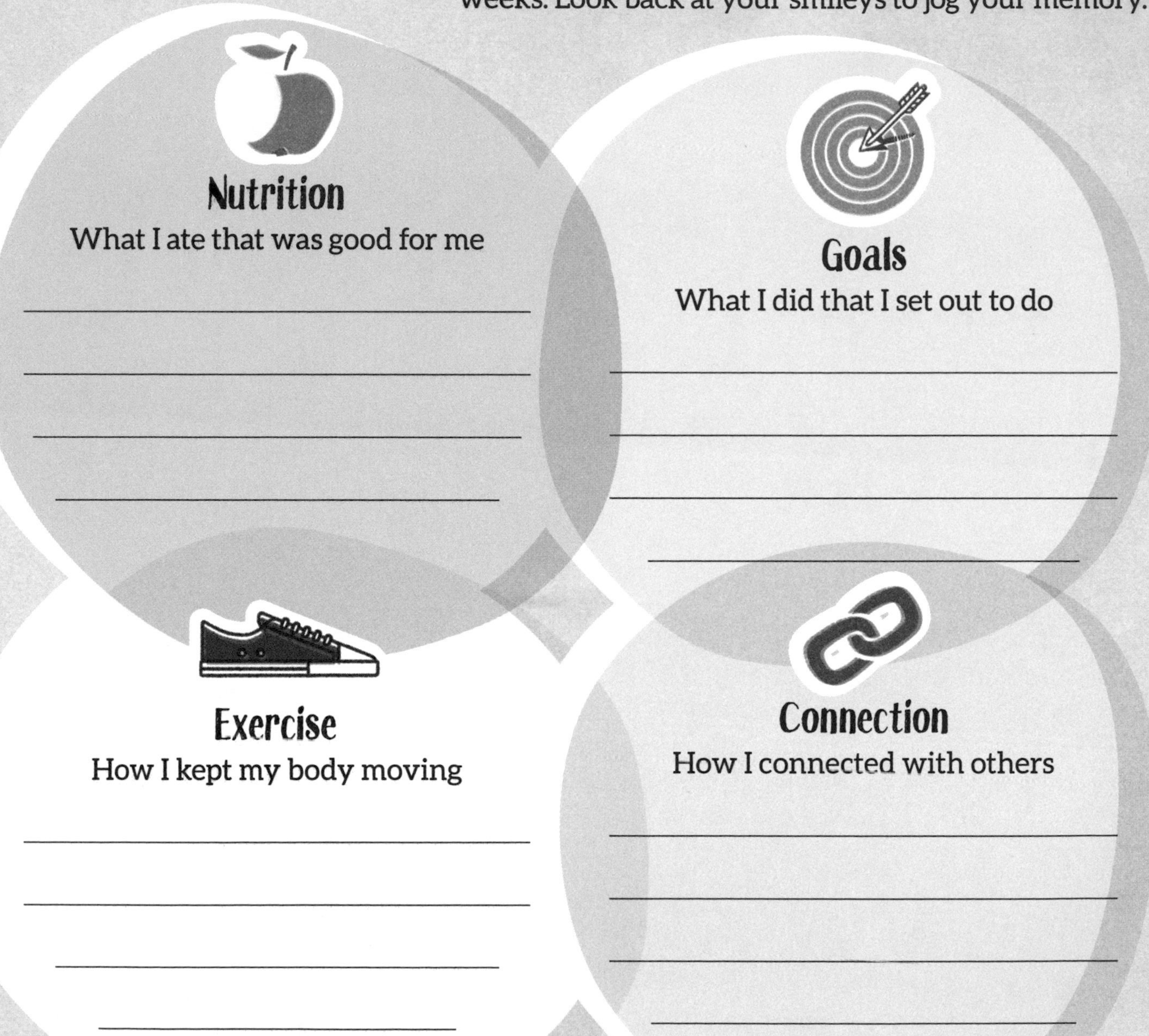

My Magic Moment A time in the last month that made me happy or proud

What I learned

___

___

How I will grow from it

___

___

When I will do it

- [ ] now
- [ ] next week
- [ ] by the end of the month
- [ ] other ___

Who I will ask to help me

___

Why they are qualified

___

___

Why my future self should be excited

___

___

Curiosity Catalyst CONSIDER THE POSSIBILITY THAT THE JOURNEY IS THE ULTIMATE PRIZE.

What if you had more energy every day?

Regular exercise pumps you up. It gives you energy. And who couldn't use more of that?

If you're already active, how can you inspire others to start moving and share in the perks of fitness?

____

____

____

If you're not active, how can you get moving and who can help?

____

____

____

"IT DOES NOT MATTER HOW SLOWLY YOU GO, AS LONG AS YOU DO NOT STOP."

CONFUCIUS

Wisdom of the Week

What did you do this week to inspire others – or yourself – to be more active? What worked well? What didn't?

How did you feel after exercising?

30 SUNDAY

31 MONDAY Tisha B'Av

1 TUESDAY

2 WEDNESDAY

3 THURSDAY

4 FRIDAY

5 SATURDAY

Well-Being Check-In

- I kept my body moving
- I ate what's good for me
- I connected with others
- I did what I set out to do

S	M	T	W	T	F	S
30	31	1	2	3	4	5
6	7	8	9	10	11	12
13	14	15	16	17	18	19
20	21	22	23	24	25	26
27	28	29	30	31	1	2

What if you replaced your kryptonite with spinach?

Each of us has something – a place, an action, a person or a belief – that gives us great strength, and something else that seems to zap our vitality.

Identify yours. This week, make a conscious effort to gravitate toward what makes you stronger, and avoid that which makes you weaker.

What gives me my greatest strength

___
___
___
___

What zaps my strength

___
___
___
___

“WHEN SOMETHING BAD HAPPENS, YOU HAVE THREE CHOICES. YOU CAN LET IT DEFINE YOU, YOU CAN LET IT DESTROY YOU, OR YOU CAN LET IT STRENGTHEN YOU.”

UNKNOWN

Wisdom of the Week

Do you consider yourself stronger or weaker now than you were years ago? Why?

6 SUNDAY

7 MONDAY

8 TUESDAY

9 WEDNESDAY

10 THURSDAY

11 FRIDAY

12 SATURDAY

Well-Being Check-In

I kept my body moving

I ate what's good for me

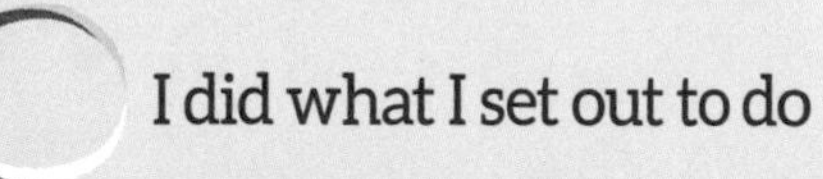

I connected with others

I did what I set out to do

S	M	T	W	T	F	S
30	31	1	2	3	4	5
6	7	8	9	10	11	12
13	14	15	16	17	18	19
20	21	22	23	24	25	26
27	28	29	30	31	1	2

How handy are your hands?

Let's put your non-dominant hand to work. If you are right-handed, this is your left hand's chance to shine. If you are left-handed, don't think you are getting off easy – you are going to use your right hand for this exercise.

Start with the hand you typically write with and follow the instructions for each section in that column. Then switch hands and complete the other column.

Draw a square, circle and star	*Draw a square, circle and star*
Print your name	*Print your name*
Draw a dog	*Draw a dog*
Draw a happy pineapple riding a bicycle	*Draw a happy pineapple riding a bicycle*

"If the left side of your brain controls the right side of your body, and the right side of your brain controls the left side of your body, then left-handed people must be the only ones in their right minds."

W.C. Fields

Wisdom of the Week

Why do you think we often "default" to certain ways of doing things even when we are capable of trying others?

13 SUNDAY Spirit of '45 Day (U.S.)
International Left-Handers Day

14 MONDAY

15 TUESDAY

16 WEDNESDAY

17 THURSDAY

18 FRIDAY

19 SATURDAY

Well-Being Check-In

I kept my body moving

I ate what's good for me

I connected with others

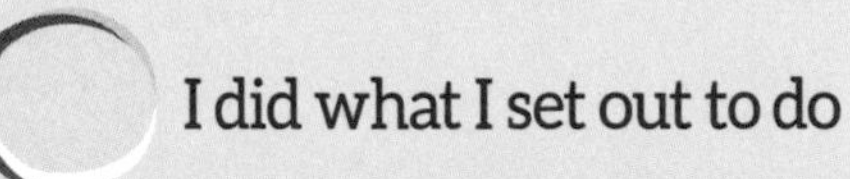

I did what I set out to do

S	M	T	W	T	F	S
30	31	1	2	3	4	5
6	7	8	9	10	11	12
13	14	15	16	17	18	19
20	21	22	23	24	25	26
27	28	29	30	31	1	2

Try to take a load off your soul.

Whether it is for a recent spat or a long-simmering issue, forgiving someone can be a cathartic experience. Carefully choose someone to forgive this week. Think about whether the person really meant to hurt you or if it was unintentional. Consider how holding on to bitterness has affected you.

What's the worst that could happen? More important, what's the best?

The Worst That Could Happen

1. ______________________
2. ______________________

The Best That Could Happen

1. ______________________
2. ______________________
3. ______________________
4. ______________________
5. ______________________
6. ______________________

“Forgiveness is the fragrance that the violet sheds on the heel that has crushed it.”

Unknown

Wisdom of the Week

Do you struggle with forgiveness? If so, describe how.

Did you have any breakthroughs this week?

20 SUNDAY

21 MONDAY

22 TUESDAY

23 WEDNESDAY

24 THURSDAY

25 FRIDAY Kiss and Make Up Day

26 SATURDAY Women's Equality Day (U.S.)

Well-Being Check-In

I kept my body moving

I ate what's good for me

I connected with others

I did what I set out to do

S	M	T	W	T	F	S
30	31	1	2	3	4	5
6	7	8	9	10	11	12
13	14	15	16	17	18	19
20	21	22	23	24	25	26
27	28	29	30	31	1	2

How well is your being?

Four fascinating weeks have flown by.

Before you charge full steam ahead into next month, take some time to focus your inquisitiveness inward – to your own well-being.

Sum up your four key lifestyle choices over the last four weeks. Look back at your smileys to jog your memory.

Nutrition

What I ate that was good for me

___

___

___

___

Goals

What I did that I set out to do

___

___

___

___

Exercise

How I kept my body moving

___

___

___

___

Connection

How I connected with others

___

___

___

___

My Magic Moment A time in the last month that made me happy or proud

___

What I learned

How I will grow from it

When I will do it

- [ ] now
- [ ] next week
- [ ] by the end of the month
- [ ] other ______

Who I will ask to help me

Why they are qualified

Why my future self should be excited

Curiosity Catalyst IF THERE WERE A TRANSCRIPT OF EVERYTHING YOU'VE EVER SAID IN YOUR ENTIRE LIFE, WHAT WORD WOULD COME UP MOST FREQUENTLY?

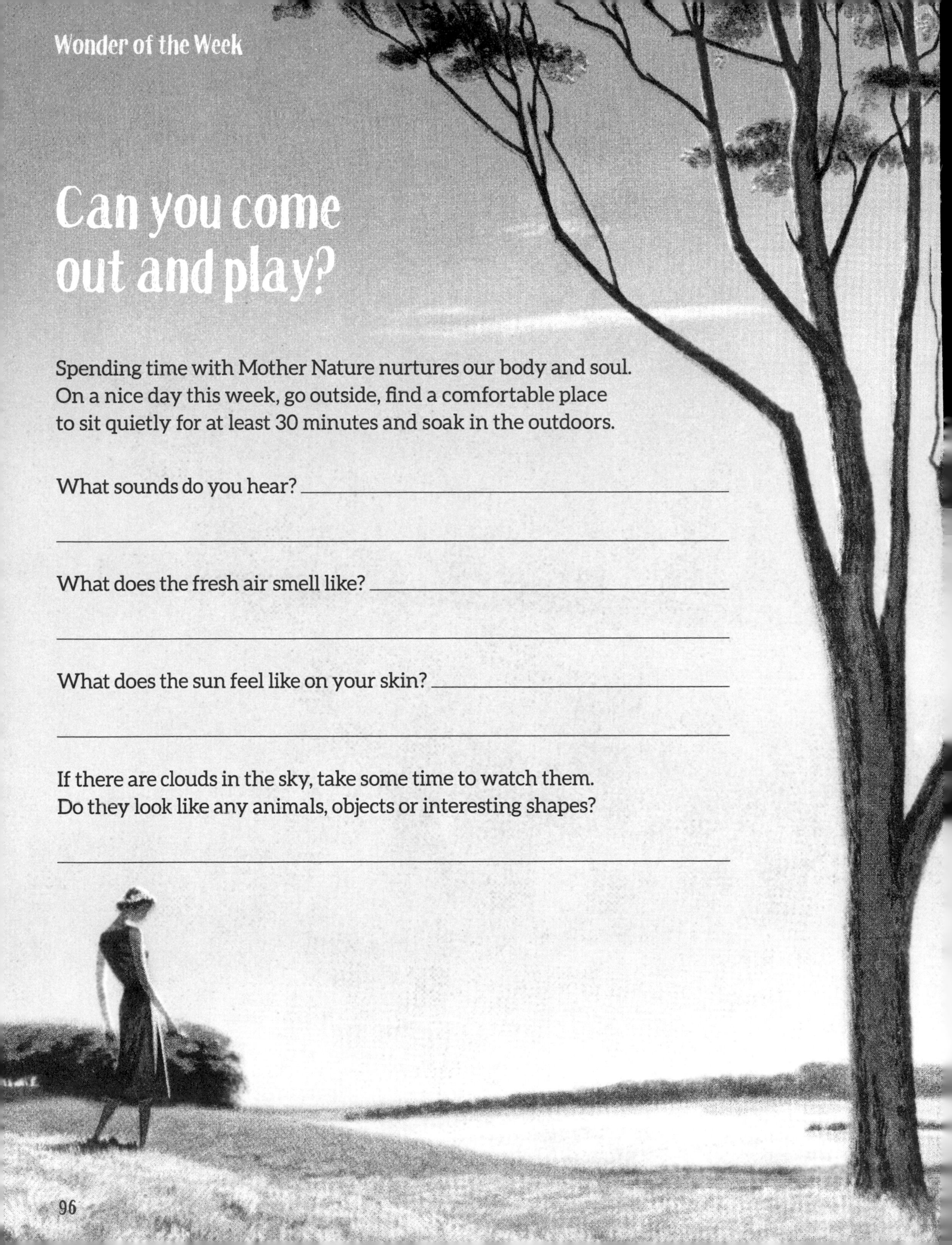

Can you come out and play?

Spending time with Mother Nature nurtures our body and soul. On a nice day this week, go outside, find a comfortable place to sit quietly for at least 30 minutes and soak in the outdoors.

What sounds do you hear? ______________________________

____

What does the fresh air smell like? ______________________________

____

What does the sun feel like on your skin? ______________________________

____

If there are clouds in the sky, take some time to watch them. Do they look like any animals, objects or interesting shapes?

____

"IN EVERY WALK WITH NATURE ONE RECEIVES FAR MORE THAN HE SEEKS."

JOHN MUIR

27 SUNDAY

28 MONDAY

29 TUESDAY

30 WEDNESDAY

31 THURSDAY

1 FRIDAY

2 SATURDAY

Wisdom of the Week

How do you feel when you are out in nature?

What type of natural surroundings do you prefer? Why?

Well-Being Check-In

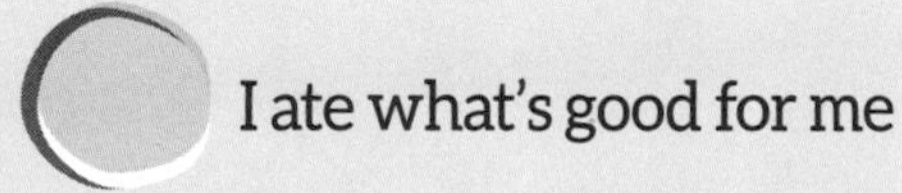

- I kept my body moving
- I ate what's good for me
- I connected with others
- I did what I set out to do

S	M	T	W	T	F	S
30	31	1	2	3	4	5
6	7	8	9	10	11	12
13	14	15	16	17	18	19
20	21	22	23	24	25	26
27	28	29	30	31	1	2

What if you gave it away?

All our lives, we gather, we buy, we collect and we receive. But the longer we live, the more we realize that the best stuff in life isn't stuff at all.

Choose one object you own. Think about the story of how you came to possess it, how long you've had it, how you've used it and what it means to you.

Now think about someone else who could really use, appreciate or benefit from the object. They can be someone you know or someone you don't. Then give the object to them, freely and unconditionally.

"GIVE WHAT YOU HAVE. TO SOMEONE, IT MAY BE BETTER THAN YOU DARE TO THINK."

HENRY WADSWORTH LONGFELLOW

Wisdom of the Week

How did it feel to let go of your object and realize you won't have it anymore?

___

___

How did it feel to know that someone else would have something useful, meaningful or delightful because of your thoughtfulness? How do you think they felt receiving it?

___

___

___

___

3 SUNDAY

___

___

4 MONDAY Labor Day

___

___

5 TUESDAY

___

___

6 WEDNESDAY

___

___

7 THURSDAY

___

___

8 FRIDAY

___

___

9 SATURDAY

___

___

Well-Being Check-In

I kept my body moving

I ate what's good for me

I connected with others

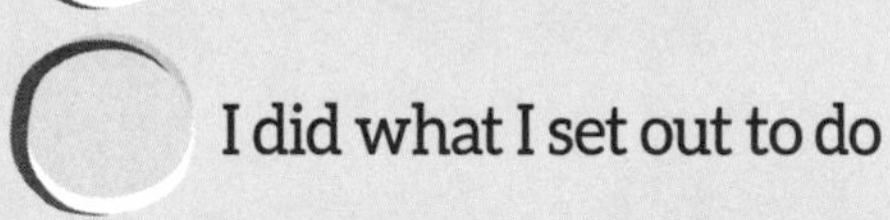

I did what I set out to do

S	M	T	W	T	F	S
27	28	29	30	31	1	2
3	4	5	6	7	8	9
10	11	12	13	14	15	16
17	18	19	20	21	22	23
24	25	26	27	28	29	30

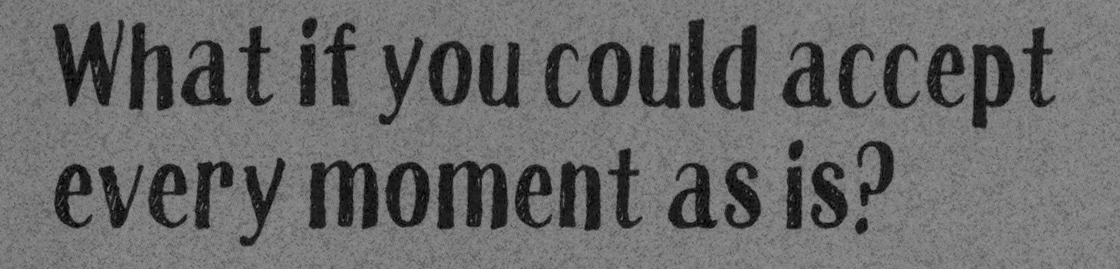

What if you could accept every moment as is?

Mindfulness means focusing on the present moment exactly as it is – without judging it or trying to change it.

This week, set aside a few minutes a day to sit quietly and meditate. Breathe normally and pay attention to each breath while letting your thoughts come and go without latching onto them. When your mind wanders – and it will – gently ease your attention back to your breath.

"FEELINGS COME AND GO LIKE CLOUDS IN A WINDY SKY. CONSCIOUS BREATHING IS MY ANCHOR."

THICH NHAT HANH

Wisdom of the Week

What's one thing you discovered about yourself while meditating this week?

What did you find most difficult about meditating?

10 SUNDAY Grandparents Day (U.S.)

11 MONDAY Patriot Day (U.S.)

12 TUESDAY Mindfulness Day

13 WEDNESDAY

14 THURSDAY

15 FRIDAY

16 SATURDAY

Well-Being Check-In

I kept my body moving

I ate what's good for me

I connected with others

I did what I set out to do

S	M	T	W	T	F	S
27	28	29	30	31	1	2
3	4	5	6	7	8	9
10	11	12	13	14	15	16
17	18	19	20	21	22	23
24	25	26	27	28	29	30

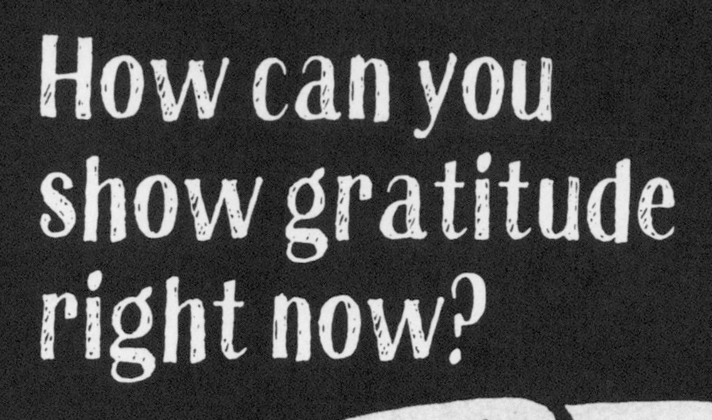

How can you show gratitude right now?

It's been said that gratitude is the most accessible of all wisdoms. It costs the least to give, yields the biggest return – and we can give it anytime, in any situation.

This week, stretch your gratitude muscles extra hard and show appreciation to the people who enrich your day-to-day life. Think about specific ways each person makes your day brighter, and give them sincere, thoughtful recognition. Set a goal to express your gratitude three times a day.

"Nothing that is done for you is a matter of course. Everything originates in a will for the good, which is directed at you. Train yourself never to put off the word or action for the expression of gratitude."

Albert Schweitzer

Wisdom of the Week

How did sharing your appreciation for others affect your mood? Do you feel happier?

____

____

____

What expression of gratitude made the biggest impact?

____

____

____

17 SUNDAY

18 MONDAY

19 TUESDAY

20 WEDNESDAY Rosh Hashanah Begins

21 THURSDAY World Gratitude Day

22 FRIDAY Rosh Hashanah Ends

23 SATURDAY

Well-Being Check-In

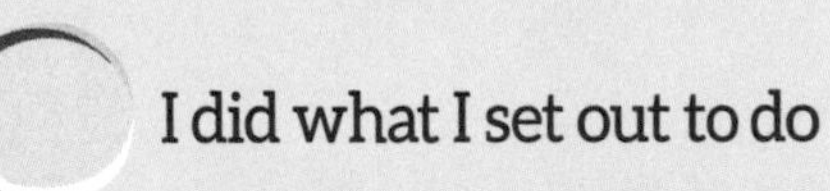

- I kept my body moving
- I ate what's good for me
- I connected with others
- I did what I set out to do

S	M	T	W	T	F	S
27	28	29	30	31	1	2
3	4	5	6	7	8	9
10	11	12	13	14	15	16
17	18	19	20	21	22	23
24	25	26	27	28	29	30

What if being a nosy neighbor were a good thing?

Sure, "nosy" can mean "intrusive" or "meddlesome." But it's also another word for "curious" or "inquisitive."

This week, be nosy with your neighbors in a good way. Visit with your next-door neighbors and their next-door neighbors, and learn at least one new thing about them.

Get together with a group of your neighbors and work to identify a subject that none of you knows anything about. Come up with a way to learn about it together.

“I keep six honest serving-men (They taught me all I knew); Their names are What and Why and When and How and Where and Who.”

Rudyard Kipling

24 SUNDAY Active Aging Week

25 MONDAY

26 TUESDAY

27 WEDNESDAY

28 THURSDAY Good Neighbor Day

29 FRIDAY Yom Kippur

30 SATURDAY

Wisdom of the Week

What's the most interesting thing you learned about one of your neighbors? Did you learn anything you wish you hadn't?

Did you grow up close to neighbors or far apart? Did that influence where you chose to live as an adult?

Well-Being Check-In

I kept my body moving

I ate what's good for me

I connected with others

I did what I set out to do

S	M	T	W	T	F	S
27	28	29	30	31	1	2
3	4	5	6	7	8	9
10	11	12	13	14	15	16
17	18	19	20	21	22	23
24	25	26	27	28	29	30

How well is your being?

Five fascinating weeks have flown by.

Before you charge full steam ahead into next month, take some time to focus your inquisitiveness inward – to your own well-being.

Sum up your four key lifestyle choices over the last five weeks. Look back at your smileys to jog your memory.

My Magic Moment A time in the last month that made me happy or proud

What I learned

____

____

How I will grow from it

____

____

When I will do it

- [ ] now
- [ ] next week
- [ ] by the end of the month
- [ ] other ____________

Who I will ask to help me

____

Why they are qualified

____

____

Why my future self should be excited

____

____

Curiosity Catalyst

WHAT IF DOGS ARE ONLY PRETENDING NOT TO BE ABLE TO TALK?

Try to eat a whole rainbow of fruits and vegetables.

Fruits and vegetables aren't just randomly colorful – each hue is a clue to the specific nutrients within. The more colors you eat, the broader the spectrum of health benefits.

Brighten your week with a variety of fresh fruits and vibrant veggies, and color them in as you go. Even better, see if you can complete a double rainbow.

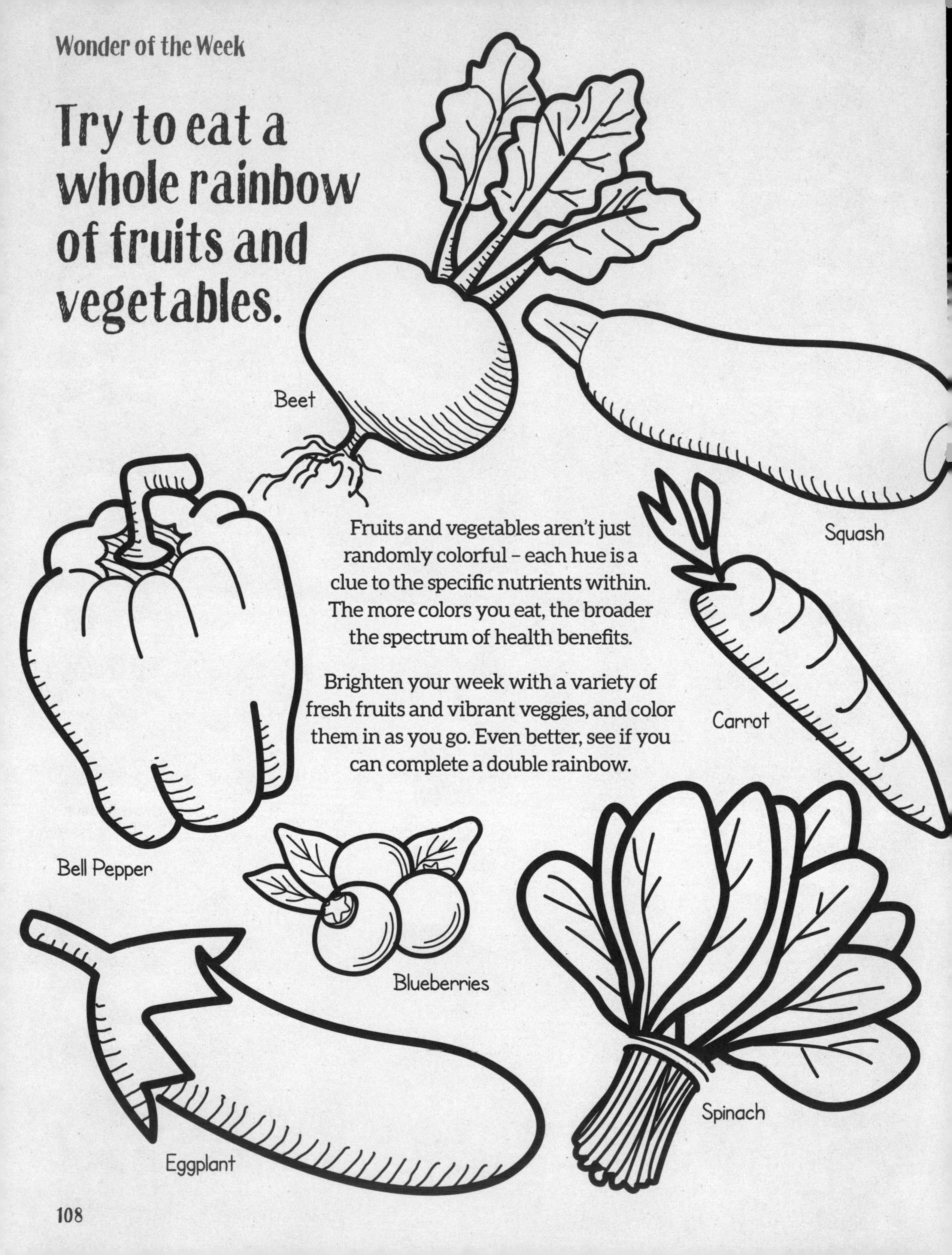

“LET FOOD BE THY MEDICINE AND MEDICINE BE THY FOOD.”

HIPPOCRATES

Wisdom of the Week

Did you try any new fruits and vegetables? Did you end up enjoying any you always thought you disliked?

Did you feel better than usual this week? Describe.

SUNDAY World Vegetarian Day

MONDAY

TUESDAY

WEDNESDAY Sukkot Begins

THURSDAY

FRIDAY

7

SATURDAY

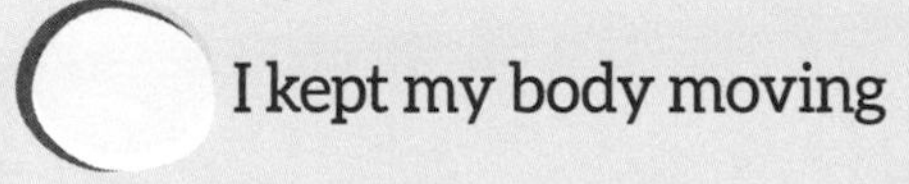

Well-Being Check-In

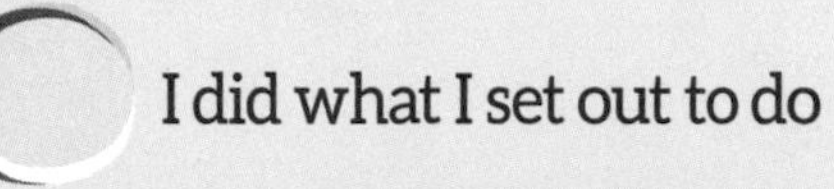

I kept my body moving

I ate what's good for me

I connected with others

I did what I set out to do

S	M	T	W	T	F	S
1	2	3	4	5	6	7
8	9	10	11	12	13	14
15	16	17	18	19	20	21
22	23	24	25	26	27	28
29	30	31	1	2	3	4

Turn nothing into something.

Take a pen or marker and place the tip of it anywhere in the blank space below. *Without looking or picking the tip up off the page*, move the pen or marker around to create a random pattern.

Now make a masterpiece. Use your imagination and let the shape of your pattern inspire you. Pick up your drawing utensils and turn the random strokes into a picture. Feel free to add some color to turn what was once disorder into a display of artistry.

"NOTHING LISTENS AS WELL AS A BLANK PAGE."

SHAUN HICK

Wisdom of the Week

In what practical life situations can you apply the skill of turning what appcars meaningless into purposeful, or messy into beautiful?

If you haven't sent it already, find the "Accidental Masterpiece" postcard in the back pocket of this planner. Start another doodle and send it to a friend to finish.

8 SUNDAY

9 MONDAY Columbus Day (U.S.)
Thanksgiving (Canada)

10 TUESDAY

11 WEDNESDAY Sukkot Ends
Shemini Atzeret

12 THURSDAY Simchat Torah

13 FRIDAY

14 SATURDAY

Well-Being Check-In

I kept my body moving

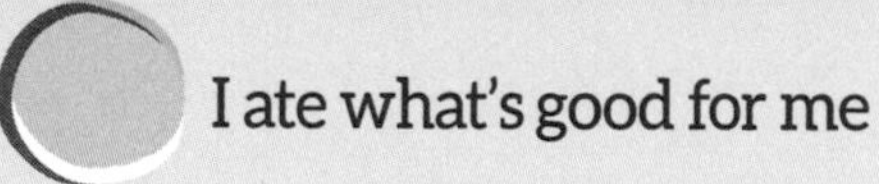

I connected with others

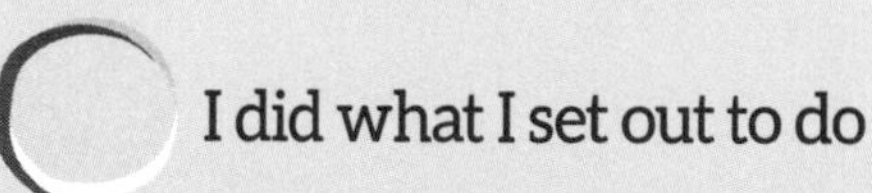

S	M	T	W	T	F	S
1	2	3	4	5	6	7
8	9	10	11	12	13	14
15	16	17	18	19	20	21
22	23	24	25	26	27	28
29	30	31	1	2	3	4

What if you could go back and name yourself?

HELLO
MY NAME IS

Our names are our birthright. They identify us to the world, shape our self-esteem and can even influence how others treat us.

If you could go back before you were born and decide your own name, what would you choose? Why? Would any aspects of your life have been different with that name?

"A human being's name is a principal component of his person, perhaps a piece of his soul."

Sigmund Freud

Fun fact: Freud changed his own first name from "Sigismund" to "Sigmund."

Wisdom of the Week

Look in the mirror and introduce yourself by the name you chose. Do you still like it? How does it feel?

Do you have any nicknames? Who gave them to you? Do you like them?

15 SUNDAY

16 MONDAY

17 TUESDAY

18 WEDNESDAY

19 THURSDAY

20 FRIDAY

21 SATURDAY

Well-Being Check-In

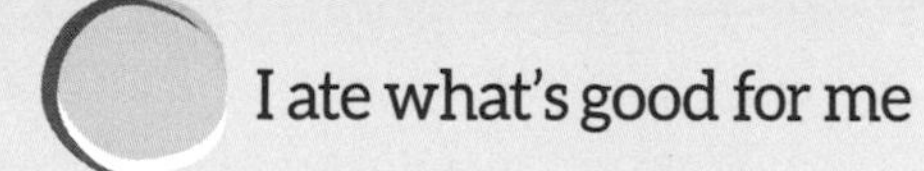

- I kept my body moving
- I ate what's good for me
- I connected with others
- I did what I set out to do

S	M	T	W	T	F	S
1	2	3	4	5	6	7
8	9	10	11	12	13	14
15	16	17	18	19	20	21
22	23	24	25	26	27	28
29	30	31	1	2	3	4

What can you do this week to make a difference?

Every day, each of us receives the same gift – 24 hours. How can you spend your gift of time to benefit others? It requires little of us to wish for a better world, but giving of ourselves through volunteering turns our wishes into actions.

Think of a person or organization you could be of service to this week. Contact them and see how the gift of your time could help fill a need and make a difference.

"HOW WONDERFUL IT IS THAT NOBODY NEED WAIT A SINGLE MOMENT BEFORE STARTING TO IMPROVE THE WORLD."

ANNE FRANK

22 SUNDAY

23 MONDAY

24 TUESDAY

25 WEDNESDAY

26 THURSDAY

27 FRIDAY

28 SATURDAY Make A Difference Day

Wisdom of the Week

How did your volunteering effort go? How did it make you feel?

Is volunteering a regular practice for you? If so, when and why did you make it part of your life?

Well-Being Check-In

- I kept my body moving
- I ate what's good for me
- I connected with others
- I did what I set out to do

S	M	T	W	T	F	S
1	2	3	4	5	6	7
8	9	10	11	12	13	14
15	16	17	18	19	20	21
22	23	24	25	26	27	28
29	30	31	1	2	3	4

How well is your being?

Four fascinating weeks have flown by.

Before you charge full steam ahead into next month, take some time to focus your inquisitiveness inward – to your own well-being.

Sum up your four key lifestyle choices over the last four weeks. Look back at your smileys to jog your memory.

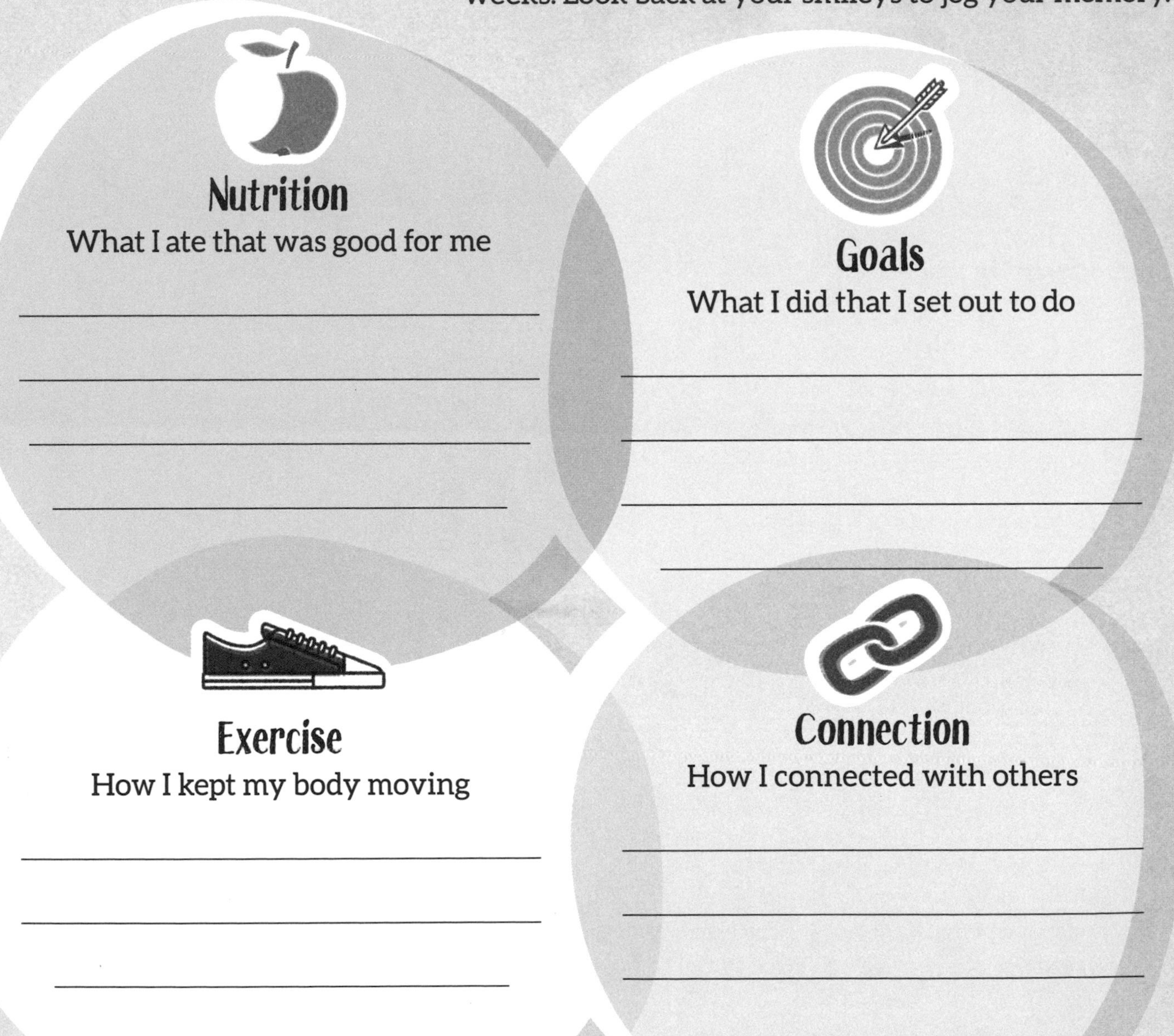

My Magic Moment A time in the last month that made me happy or proud

What I learned

How I will grow from it

When I will do it

- [ ] now
- [ ] next week
- [ ] by the end of the month
- [ ] other ____________

Who I will ask to help me

Why they are qualified

Why my future self should be excited

Curiosity Catalyst

WHAT IF YOUR LIFE'S GREATEST ACHIEVEMENT IS STILL TO COME?

Can you make fear be afraid of you?

What are you most afraid of? Snakes? Heights? Speaking in front of crowds?

1. Make a list of what scares you most.
2. Make a list of things you were once afraid of, but aren't anymore. What changed?
3. Pick one fear from the first list and circle it. Then, write next to it what you can do this week to face that fear so you can move it to the second list.

What I'm most afraid of

____

____

____

____

What I'm no longer afraid of

____

____

____

____

____

“The cave you fear to enter holds the treasure you seek.”

Joseph Campbell

Wisdom of the Week

Which fear did you face this week and what happened?

Which of your fears is the least realistic? If you know it's unrealistic, why does it continue to frighten you?

29 SUNDAY

30 MONDAY

31 TUESDAY Halloween

1 WEDNESDAY

2 THURSDAY

3 FRIDAY

4 SATURDAY

Well-Being Check-In

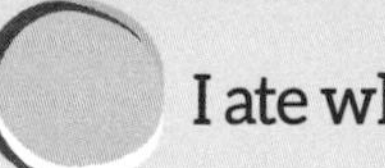

I kept my body moving

I ate what's good for me

I connected with others

I did what I set out to do

S	M	T	W	T	F	S
29	30	31	1	2	3	4
5	6	7	8	9	10	11
12	13	14	15	16	17	18
19	20	21	22	23	24	25
26	27	28	29	30	1	2

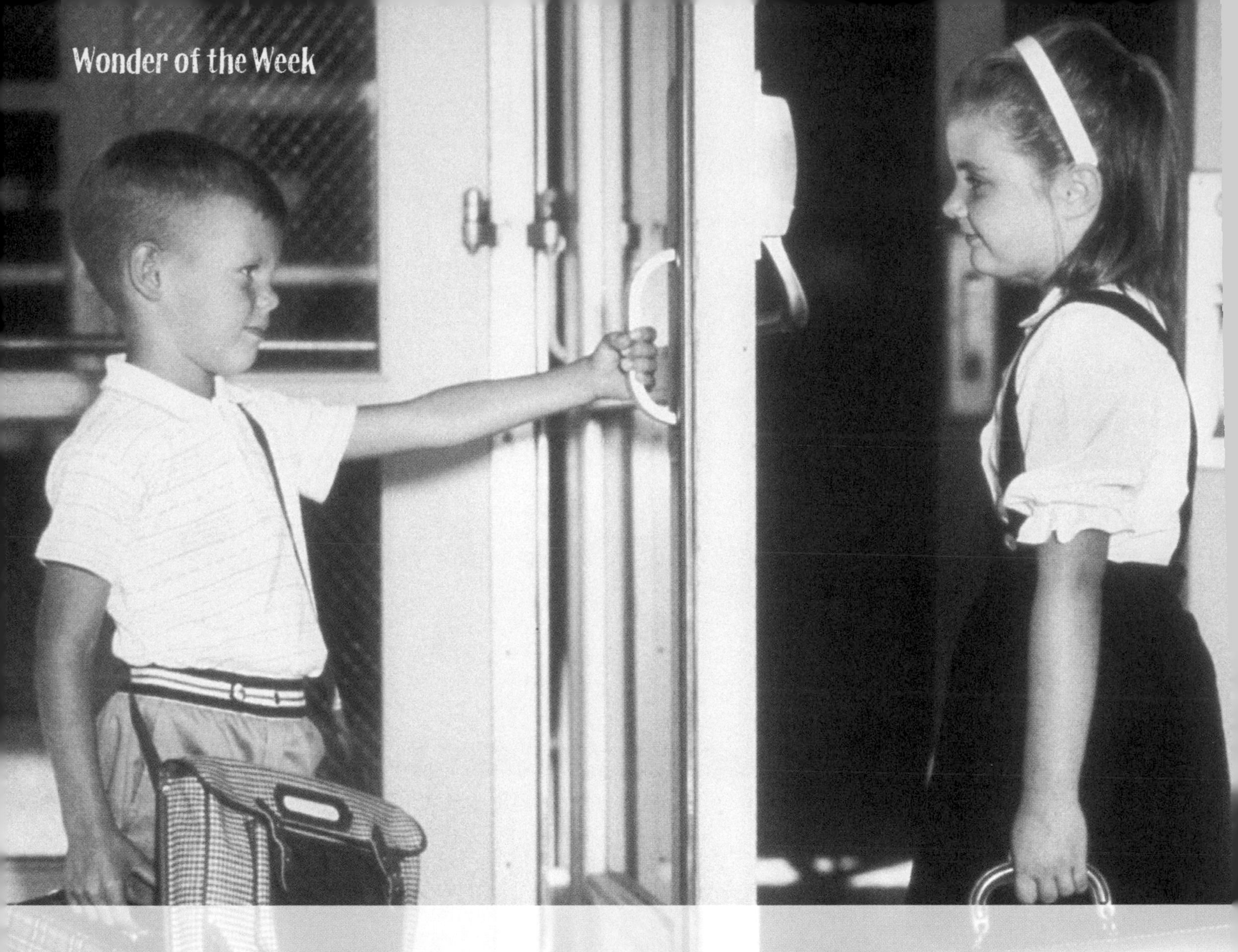

What would the world be like without people willing to serve others?

Picking up litter or holding a door open are two simple ways to be of service every day. Volunteering to build homes for the less fortunate or enlisting in the military to protect and defend your country are committed, long-term acts of service. Big or small, they all make an impact.

Focus on being of service to others this week. Below, list the people you will serve and how you plan to serve them.

1. ______________________________

____

2. ______________________________

____

3. ______________________________

____

“I SLEPT AND DREAMT THAT LIFE WAS JOY. I AWOKE AND SAW THAT LIFE WAS SERVICE. I ACTED AND BEHOLD, SERVICE WAS JOY.”

RABINDRANATH TAGORE

Wisdom of the Week

How did it feel to be of service to others this week?

____

____

____

What act of service did you find most rewarding? Why?

____

____

____

5 SUNDAY Daylight Saving Time Ends

____

____

6 MONDAY

____

____

7 TUESDAY Election Day (U.S.)

____

____

8 WEDNESDAY

____

____

9 THURSDAY

____

____

10 FRIDAY

____

____

11 SATURDAY Veterans Day (U.S.)

Remembrance Day (Canada)

____

Well-Being Check-In

I kept my body moving

I ate what's good for me

I connected with others

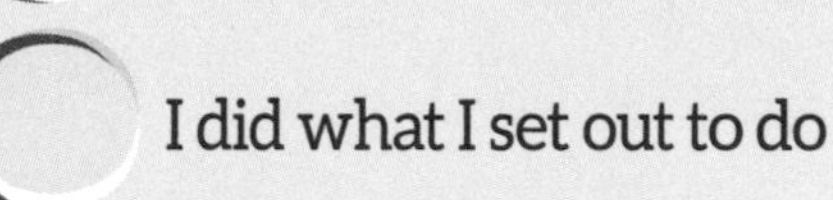

I did what I set out to do

S	M	T	W	T	F	S
29	30	31	1	2	3	4
5	6	7	8	9	10	11
12	13	14	15	16	17	18
19	20	21	22	23	24	25
26	27	28	29	30	1	2

How bright could you make someone's face light up?

Pick one person you care about. If money and time were no object, how would you lavish them in tailor-made kindness?

Think beyond just what things you would buy. Think about their favorite things to do and what's most important to them.

Thinking of that same person, identify at least one thing you really can do to be thoughtful, generous and considerate to them this week.

"NO ACT OF KINDNESS, NO MATTER HOW SMALL, IS EVER WASTED."

AESOP

12 SUNDAY

13 MONDAY World Kindness Day

14 TUESDAY

15 WEDNESDAY

16 THURSDAY

17 FRIDAY

18 SATURDAY

Wisdom of the Week

What gets in the way of being kind to everyone all the time? How can we overcome those obstacles?

Well-Being Check-In

I kept my body moving

I ate what's good for me

I connected with others

I did what I set out to do

S	M	T	W	T	F	S
29	30	31	1	2	3	4
5	6	7	8	9	10	11
12	13	14	15	16	17	18
19	20	21	22	23	24	25
26	27	28	29	30	1	2

Why not save a little room for a slice of Thanks-receiving?

While you count your blessings, stop and consider all the people who are thankful for you and why.

"APPRECIATION IS A WONDERFUL THING; IT MAKES WHAT IS EXCELLENT IN OTHERS BELONG TO US AS WELL."

VOLTAIRE

Wisdom of the Week

Did you find it uncomfortable to think of others being thankful for you? If so, why do you think it's difficult for us to receive the same sentiment that we so readily give?

19 SUNDAY

20 MONDAY

21 TUESDAY

22 WEDNESDAY

23 THURSDAY Thanksgiving (U.S.)

24 FRIDAY

25 SATURDAY

Well-Being Check-In

I kept my body moving

I ate what's good for me

I connected with others

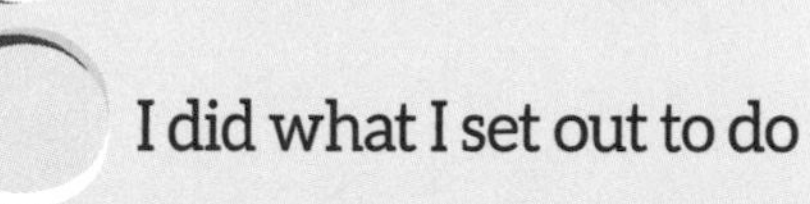

I did what I set out to do

S	M	T	W	T	F	S
29	30	31	1	2	3	4
5	6	7	8	9	10	11
12	13	14	15	16	17	18
19	20	21	22	23	24	25
26	27	28	29	30	1	2

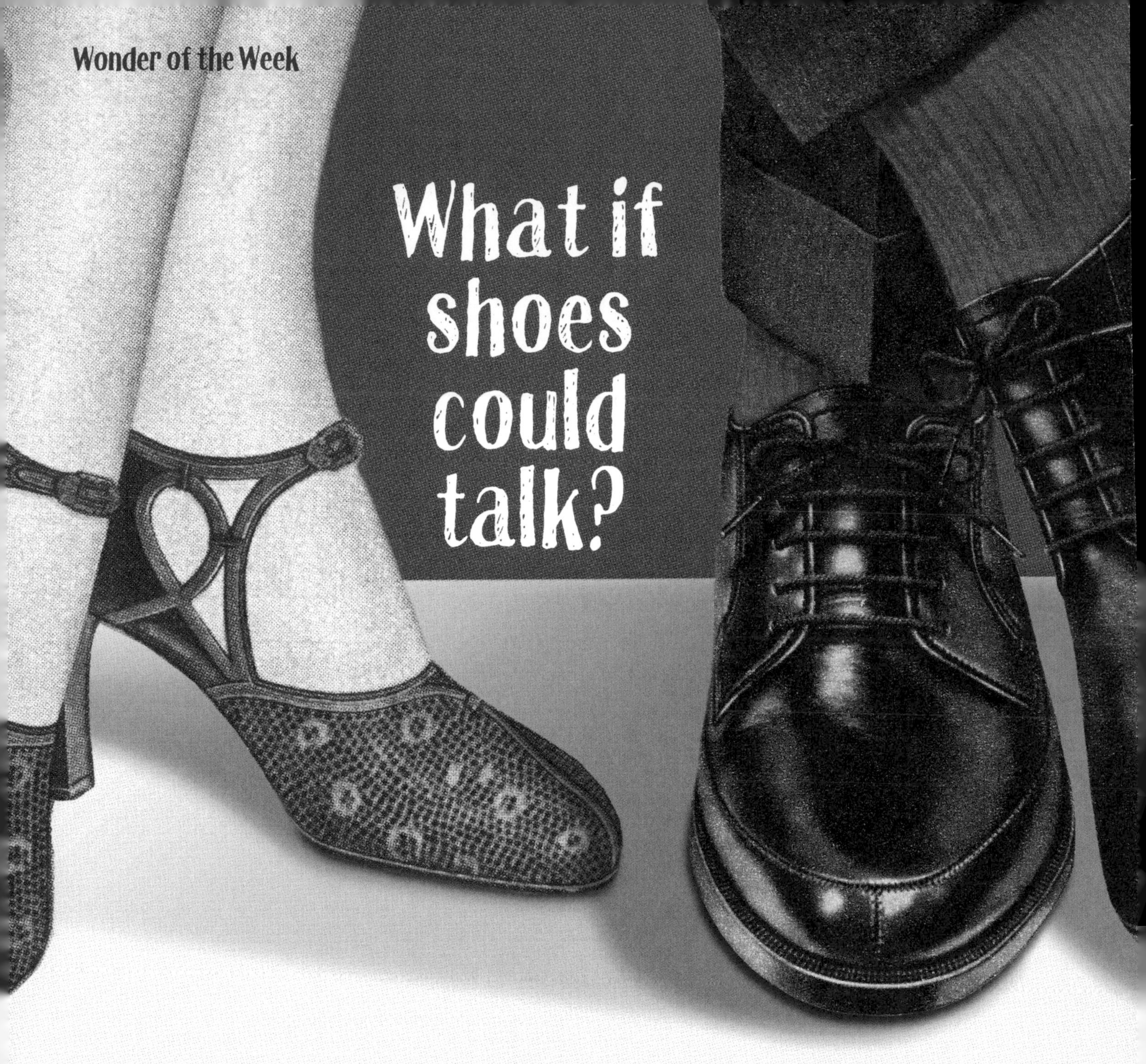

What if shoes could talk?

We all wear shoes every day without giving it too much thought. Consider how what we put on our feet tells a story about who we are and what's going on in our lives.

This week, go to a public place, have a seat and observe people, focusing on their shoes. Based solely (pun acknowledged) on their footwear, see how much you can learn about them. Ask yourself questions like: What does she do for a living? Is he healthy? Is she confident? Is he well-to-do? Is she extravagant or practical? What's important to him? Where is she going?

"WHEN YOU GREET A STRANGER, LOOK AT HIS SHOES."

MICHAEL STIPE

Wisdom of the Week

What's your favorite pair of shoes and how do they make you feel when you wear them?

Through the years, how have your shoes changed along with other aspects of your life? At what point in your life did you have the most shoes and why?

26 SUNDAY

27 MONDAY

28 TUESDAY

29 WEDNESDAY

30 THURSDAY

1 FRIDAY

2 SATURDAY

Well-Being Check-In

I kept my body moving

I ate what's good for me

I connected with others

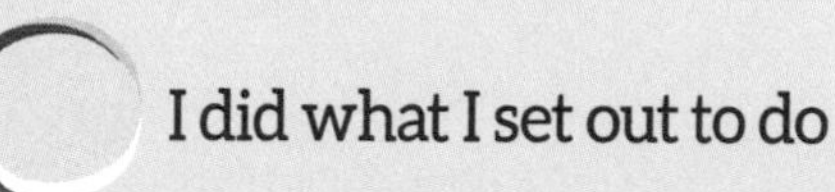

I did what I set out to do

S	M	T	W	T	F	S
29	30	31	1	2	3	4
5	6	7	8	9	10	11
12	13	14	15	16	17	18
19	20	21	22	23	24	25
26	27	28	29	30	1	2

How well is your being?

Five fascinating weeks have flown by.

Before you charge full steam ahead into next month, take some time to focus your inquisitiveness inward – to your own well-being.

Sum up your four key lifestyle choices over the last five weeks. Look back at your smileys to jog your memory.

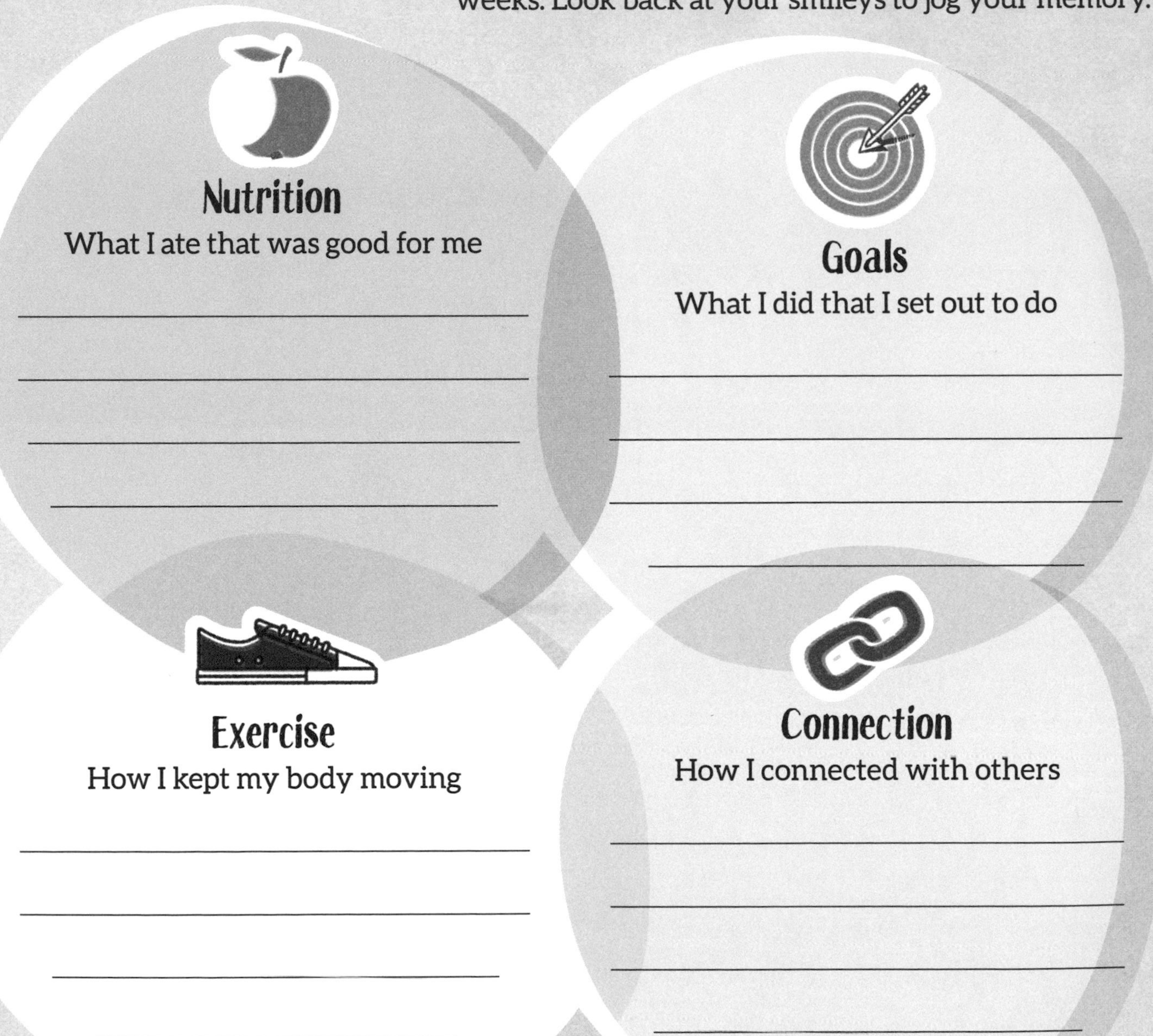

My Magic Moment A time in the last month that made me happy or proud

What I learned

____

____

How I will grow from it

____

____

When I will do it

- [ ] now
- [ ] next week
- [ ] by the end of the month
- [ ] other ____________

Who I will ask to help me

____

Why they are qualified

____

____

Why my future self should be excited

____

____

Curiosity Catalyst CONSIDER THE POSSIBILITY THAT SOMEONE'S LIFE CHANGED FOR THE BETTER BASED ON SOMETHING YOU DON'T EVEN REMEMBER SAYING.

Dare to be an everyday hero.

You may not consider yourself a hero, but someone else might. Think of a time you pushed a child on a swing or held the door open for a shopper laden with packages. Even your presence alone can be heroic in its kindness and positive energy.

This week, keep your eyes peeled for opportunities to fly in and help out. No act of kindness is too small for an everyday hero.

"Not all of us can do great things. But we can do small things with great love."

Mother Teresa

Wisdom of the Week

How did it feel to be a hero this week?

____

____

____

What was your favorite heroic act and why?

____

____

____

____

I kept my body moving

I ate what's good for me

I connected with others

I did what I set out to do

S	M	T	W	T	F	S
26	27	28	29	30	1	2
3	4	5	6	7	8	9
10	11	12	13	14	15	16
17	18	19	20	21	22	23
24	25	26	27	28	29	30
31	1	2	3	4	5	6

Dare to learn a new dance.

We dance to celebrate, express joy or simply blow off steam. From the choices below, pick a dance you've never done before or never even heard of. Then learn how to do it – either by asking a friend or family member to help you, looking up a video on the Internet or taking a class. While you're at it, why not teach someone else a dance they don't know, too?

The Bump
The Nae Nae
The Pony
The Tango
The Cabbage Patch
The Hustle
The Twist
The Charleston
The Lindy Hop
The Safety Dance
The Camel Walk
The Watusi
The Loco-Motion
The Dougie
The Bartman
The Hokey Pokey

"DANCE IS THE HIDDEN LANGUAGE OF THE SOUL."

MARTHA GRAHAM

Wisdom of the Week

What words describe how you feel while dancing? How do you feel afterward?

Would you rather be excellent at one type of dance or be adequate at many styles? Explain.

10 SUNDAY

11 MONDAY

12 TUESDAY Hanukkah Begins

13 WEDNESDAY

14 THURSDAY

15 FRIDAY

16 SATURDAY

Well-Being Check-In

I kept my body moving

I ate what's good for me

I connected with others

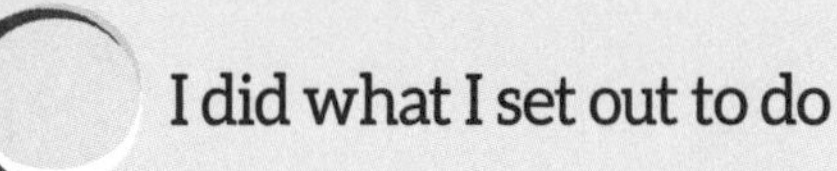

I did what I set out to do

S	M	T	W	T	F	S
26	27	28	29	30	1	2
3	4	5	6	7	8	9
10	11	12	13	14	15	16
17	18	19	20	21	22	23
24	25	26	27	28	29	30
31	1	2	3	4	5	6

Can you color your cares away?

We all experience stress sometimes. Whenever you're feeling the pressure this week, take a few moments to focus on something simple and beautiful instead.

Begin by writing what is causing you stress in the circle below ("overwhelmed" or "miss someone," for example). Then, starting in the area nearest the circle and working outward, begin to color in the drawing, calmly and methodically, for as long or briefly as you like. When you finish the entire design, color over what was causing you stress.

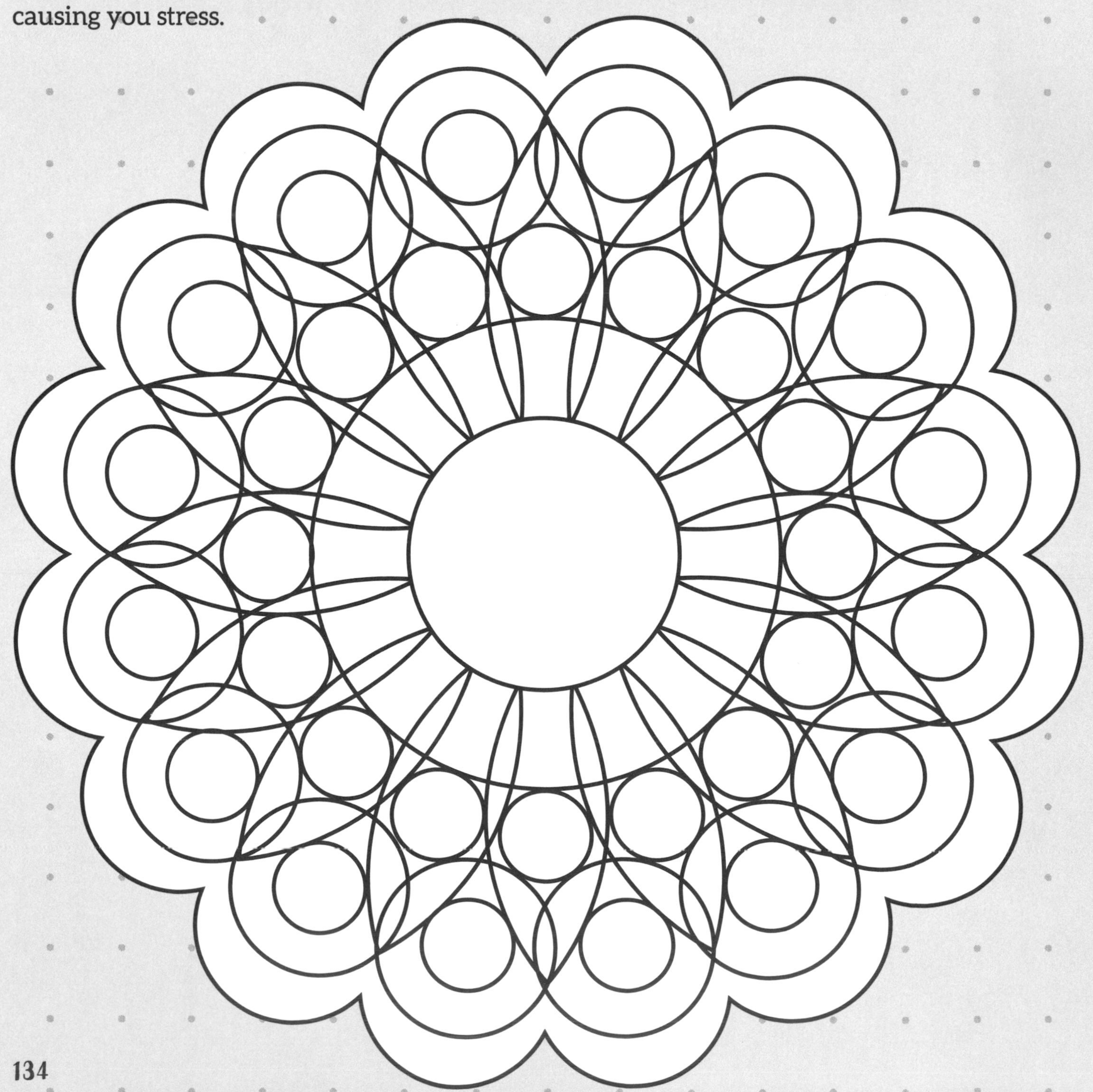

"COLOR IS THE PLACE WHERE OUR BRAIN AND THE UNIVERSE MEET."

PAUL KLEE

Wisdom of the Week

Did you find coloring therapeutic? If so, in what way?

17 SUNDAY

18 MONDAY

19 TUESDAY

20 WEDNESDAY Hanukkah Ends

21 THURSDAY

22 FRIDAY

23 SATURDAY

Well-Being Check-In

I kept my body moving

I ate what's good for me

I connected with others

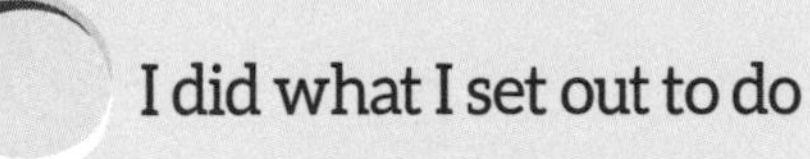

I did what I set out to do

S	M	T	W	T	F	S
26	27	28	29	30	1	2
3	4	5	6	7	8	9
10	11	12	13	14	15	16
17	18	19	20	21	22	23
24	25	26	27	28	29	30
31	1	2	3	4	5	6

What if a Martian invited himself to your holiday dinner?

He'd probably be curious about all of the happenings of the holiday season. How would you help the alien understand why human behavior changes at this time of the year? How would you explain your holiday traditions and what makes them special?

"THE LESS THERE IS TO JUSTIFY A TRADITIONAL CUSTOM, THE HARDER IT IS TO GET RID OF IT."

MARK TWAIN

SUNDAY

25 **MONDAY** Christmas

26 **TUESDAY** Boxing Day (Canada)
Kwanzaa Begins

27 **WEDNESDAY**

28 **THURSDAY**

29 **FRIDAY**

30 **SATURDAY**

Wisdom of the Week

What family holiday traditions have you kept going?

What new holiday traditions did you help introduce into your family?

Well-Being Check-In

I kept my body moving

I ate what's good for me

I connected with others

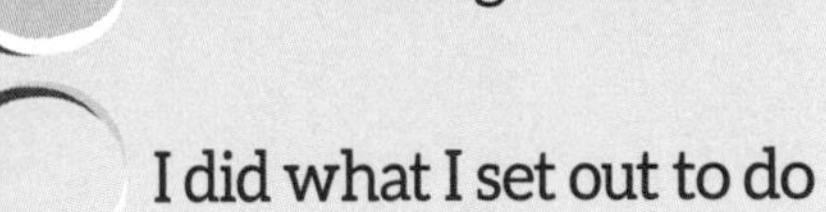

I did what I set out to do

S	M	T	W	T	F	S
26	27	28	29	30	1	2
3	4	5	6	7	8	9
10	11	12	13	14	15	16
17	18	19	20	21	22	23
24	25	26	27	28	29	30
31	1	2	3	4	5	6

Can the most curious year ever be over already?

Yes, it's true. You have asked a lot of interesting questions. You've explored. You've discovered. Most important, *you've grown*. And in the process, you have opened yourself to enjoying closer relationships and greater well-being.

Before you begin another curious trip around the sun, take time to recall and record the highlights of the one you just completed.

Most satisfying accomplishment

____

____

____

____

Most surprising discovery

____

____

____

____

Most interesting new experience

____

____

____

____

Most fun experience

____

____

____

____

Most life-changing moment

Bravest moment

Most grateful moment

Proudest moment

Wisdom of the Week

Look back at the letter from your future self on page 12. What are the similarities and differences between it and the highlights you wrote today? Describe.

31

SUNDAY

S	M	T	W	T	F	S
26	27	28	29	30	1	2
3	4	5	6	7	8	9
10	11	12	13	14	15	16
17	18	19	20	21	22	23
24	25	26	27	28	29	30
31	1	2	3	4	5	6

Nutrition

What I will eat that is good for me

What's next?

What's next is what you choose to be next.

Set your course for growth and well-being in 2018. After the remarkable year you just had, you know what to do.

Goals

What I will set out to do

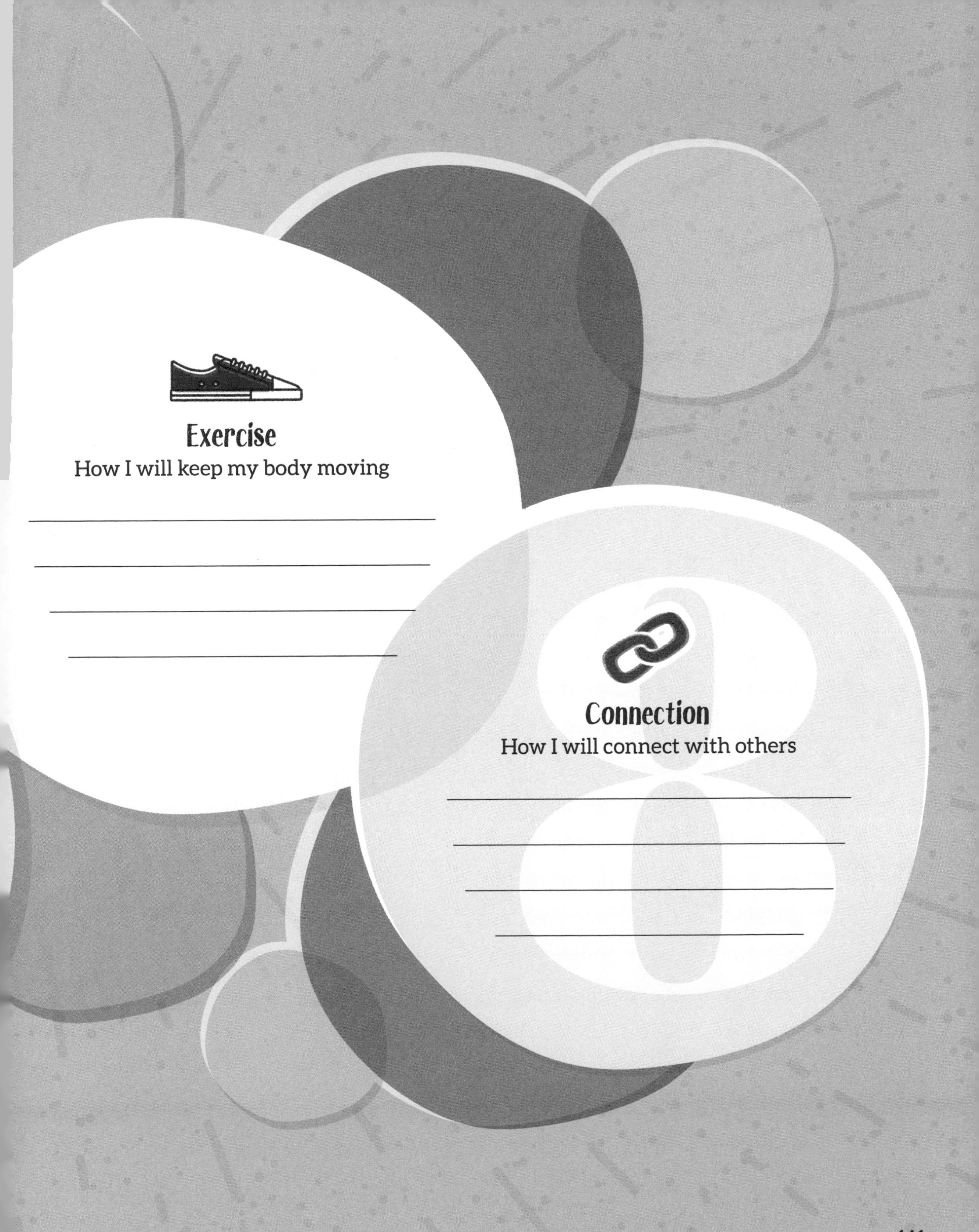

Exercise
How I will keep my body moving
Connection
How I will connect with others

What do you promise your future self?

I will focus on these top three priorities

1. ______________________________

____

2. ______________________________

____

3. ______________________________

____

I will spend more time doing this thing that makes me happy

____

____

I will spend less time doing this thing that is counterproductive

____

I will connect more with this person who uplifts me

____

I will improve upon this quality of mine

____

____

I will share my wisdom with others by

____

____

Who I will get to know this person better

____

What I will explore this subject further

____

Why I will get to the bottom of this mystery

____

Where I will learn more about this place

____

How I will figure out how this works

____

When I will inspire future generations to be curious by doing this

____

____

Keep curiosity alive. Encourage your fellow human beings to inquire, explore and discover. By setting an example with your actions and sharing the wisdom of curiosity, you are leaving a legacy that will create a more curious world for generations to come.

2018

JANUARY

S	M	T	W	T	F	S
	1	2	3	4	5	6
7	8	9	10	11	12	13
14	15	16	17	18	19	20
21	22	23	24	25	26	27
28	29	30	31			

FEBRUARY

S	M	T	W	T	F	S
				1	2	3
4	5	6	7	8	9	10
11	12	13	14	15	16	17
18	19	20	21	22	23	24
25	26	27	28			

MARCH

S	M	T	W	T	F	S
				1	2	3
4	5	6	7	8	9	10
11	12	13	14	15	16	17
18	19	20	21	22	23	24
25	26	27	28	29	30	31

APRIL

S	M	T	W	T	F	S
1	2	3	4	5	6	7
8	9	10	11	12	13	14
15	16	17	18	19	20	21
22	23	24	25	26	27	28
29	30					

MAY

S	M	T	W	T	F	S
		1	2	3	4	5
6	7	8	9	10	11	12
13	14	15	16	17	18	19
20	21	22	23	24	25	26
27	28	29	30	31		

JUNE

S	M	T	W	T	F	S
					1	2
3	4	5	6	7	8	9
10	11	12	13	14	15	16
17	18	19	20	21	22	23
24	25	26	27	28	29	30

JULY

S	M	T	W	T	F	S
1	2	3	4	5	6	7
8	9	10	11	12	13	14
15	16	17	18	19	20	21
22	23	24	25	26	27	28
29	30	31				

AUGUST

S	M	T	W	T	F	S
			1	2	3	4
5	6	7	8	9	10	11
12	13	14	15	16	17	18
19	20	21	22	23	24	25
26	27	28	29	30	31	

SEPTEMBER

S	M	T	W	T	F	S
						1
2	3	4	5	6	7	8
9	10	11	12	13	14	15
16	17	18	19	20	21	22
23	24	25	26	27	28	29
30						

OCTOBER

S	M	T	W	T	F	S
	1	2	3	4	5	6
7	8	9	10	11	12	13
14	15	16	17	18	19	20
21	22	23	24	25	26	27
28	29	30	31			

NOVEMBER

S	M	T	W	T	F	S
				1	2	3
4	5	6	7	8	9	10
11	12	13	14	15	16	17
18	19	20	21	22	23	24
25	26	27	28	29	30	

DECEMBER

S	M	T	W	T	F	S
						1
2	3	4	5	6	7	8
9	10	11	12	13	14	15
16	17	18	19	20	21	22
23	24	25	26	27	28	29
30	31					

2019

JANUARY

S	M	T	W	T	F	S
		1	2	3	4	5
6	7	8	9	10	11	12
13	14	15	16	17	18	19
20	21	22	23	24	25	26
27	28	29	30	31		

FEBRUARY

S	M	T	W	T	F	S
					1	2
3	4	5	6	7	8	9
10	11	12	13	14	15	16
17	18	19	20	21	22	23
24	25	26	27	28		

MARCH

S	M	T	W	T	F	S
					1	2
3	4	5	6	7	8	9
10	11	12	13	14	15	16
17	18	19	20	21	22	23
24	25	26	27	28	29	30
31						

APRIL

S	M	T	W	T	F	S
	1	2	3	4	5	6
7	8	9	10	11	12	13
14	15	16	17	18	19	20
21	22	23	24	25	26	27
28	29	30				

MAY

S	M	T	W	T	F	S
			1	2	3	4
5	6	7	8	9	10	11
12	13	14	15	16	17	18
19	20	21	22	23	24	25
26	27	28	29	30	31	

JUNE

S	M	T	W	T	F	S
						1
2	3	4	5	6	7	8
9	10	11	12	13	14	15
16	17	18	19	20	21	22
23	24	25	26	27	28	29
30						

JULY

S	M	T	W	T	F	S
	1	2	3	4	5	6
7	8	9	10	11	12	13
14	15	16	17	18	19	20
21	22	23	24	25	26	27
28	29	30	31			

AUGUST

S	M	T	W	T	F	S
				1	2	3
4	5	6	7	8	9	10
11	12	13	14	15	16	17
18	19	20	21	22	23	24
25	26	27	28	29	30	31

SEPTEMBER

S	M	T	W	T	F	S
1	2	3	4	5	6	7
8	9	10	11	12	13	14
15	16	17	18	19	20	21
22	23	24	25	26	27	28
29	30					

OCTOBER

S	M	T	W	T	F	S
		1	2	3	4	5
6	7	8	9	10	11	12
13	14	15	16	17	18	19
20	21	22	23	24	25	26
27	28	29	30	31		

NOVEMBER

S	M	T	W	T	F	S
					1	2
3	4	5	6	7	8	9
10	11	12	13	14	15	16
17	18	19	20	21	22	23
24	25	26	27	28	29	30

DECEMBER

S	M	T	W	T	F	S
1	2	3	4	5	6	7
8	9	10	11	12	13	14
15	16	17	18	19	20	21
22	23	24	25	26	27	28
29	30	31